TOPICS IN FIELDS AND SOLIDS

TOPICS IN FIELDS AND SOLIDS

C. ALTON COULTER
and
ROMAS A. SHATAS
Editors

GORDON AND BREACH, SCIENCE PUBLISHERS
New York • London • Paris

150 Fifth Avenue, New York, N. Y. 10011

Library of Congress Catalog Card Number: 68 - 23995

Editorial office for Great Britain:

Gordon and Breach, Science Publishers Ltd.
8 Bloomsbury Way
London W.C.1

Editorial office for France:

Gordon & Breach
7-9 rue Emile Dubois
Paris 14e

Distributed in Canada by:

The Ryerson Press
299 Queen Street West
Toronto 2B, Ontario

Printed in the United States of America

PREFACE

This book is primarily the outgrowth of a series of summer seminars in theoretical physics held at the Physical Sciences Laboratory at Redstone Arsenal, Alabama. The subject matter of these summer seminars was chosen from topics which were of interest to laboratory personnel, but which are frequently slighted in graduate physics curricula; and the discussion given in the seminars was geared to provide comprehensible and reasonably thorough introductions to these topics without, however, approaching exhaustiveness. Expanded and edited versions of some of the lectures were subsequently issued as a series of Technical Reports by the Directorate of Research and Development, U. S. Army Missile Command, and the first three papers in the present book are taken directly (except for a few minor corrections) from these reports. The fourth paper appearing here also had its origin in the seminar series just mentioned; in fact, the first three sections of the paper are a condensed version of lectures given by Romas A. Shatas at that time. However, the remainder of the sections give a discussion of original research of the authors which was presented at the Twelfth Conference of Army Mathematicians. The paper itself, aside from a few minor modifications, is taken from the Transactions of the Conference as published by the Army Research Office at Durham, North Carolina.

The authors, and particularly the editors, wish to express their appreciation to Mrs. Nancy Clem and Mrs. Hazel M. Oaks for their endless patience and invaluable aid in the typing of the manuscript.

CONTENTS

TOPICS IN
FIELDS AND SOLIDS

INTRODUCTION TO NONRELATIVISTIC QUANTUM FIELDS AND DIAGRAM TECHNIQUES

by

C. ALTON COULTER

and

B. M. MORRIS*

Solid State Physics Branch
Physical Sciences Laboratory
Research and Development Directorate
U. S. Army Missile Command
Redstone Arsenal, Alabama 35809

*Department of Physics, University of Tennessee.

ABSTRACT

Graduate-level lectures given at the 1964 Summer Seminar in Theoretical Physics at Redstone Arsenal are presented. The part abstracted here deals with the fundamentals of nonrelativistic quantum field theory. The discussion begins with a review of the Heisenberg and Schrödinger pictures in ordinary quantum mechanics, and then proceeds immediately to a development of the second-quantization formalism. Operator fields with appropriate boson and fermion equal-time commutation relations are introduced, and the details of the mathematical representation and physical interpretation are worked out for the case of noninteracting particles. The theory is then extended to embrace two-body particle-conserving interactions, and finally particle-nonconserving interactions are treated. The method for obtaining alternative forms of the theory by expanding the field operators in terms of complete orthonormal sets of functions is discussed. The integral equation of motion in the interaction picture is developed, and its solution is obtained by successive approximations. The Dyson chronological operator is defined. Examples of time-independent and time-dependent perturbation theory in the interaction picture are given. Ordinary and chronological contractions of operator products are defined, and the use of Wick's theorem in an evaluation of the perturbation expansion for the ground state energy of a system of interacting fermions is described. The representation of the perturbation expansion by Goldstone diagrams is explained.

TABLE OF CONTENTS

Section I. INTRODUCTION TO NONRELATIVISTIC QUANTUM FIELD THEORY

by

C. Alton Coulter

1. The Heisenberg and Schrödinger Pictures in Nonrelativistic Quantum Mechanics

Ordinary nonrelativistic quantum theory can be formulated in terms of two equivalent pictures. In the first of these, called the Schrödinger picture, the state of a physical system is described by a time-dependent state vector $|\psi_s(t)\rangle$ in an appropriate Hilbert space. The behavior of this state vector as a function of time is governed by the Schrödinger equation,

$$i\hbar \frac{d}{dt} |\psi_s(t)\rangle = H|\psi_s(t)\rangle,$$

where H is the energy operator or Hamiltonian for the system. It usually is the case that H can be chosen time-independent, and when this is so the Schrödinger state $|\psi_s(t)\rangle$ at time t is given in terms of the Schrödinger state $|\psi_s(0)\rangle$ at time 0 by the relation

$$|\psi_s(t)\rangle = e^{-\frac{i}{\hbar}Ht} |\psi_s(0)\rangle.$$

The expectation value of an operator F_s at time t - which, if F_s is Hermitian, represents the result of a physical measurement on the system at time t - is by definition

$$\langle \psi_s(t)|F_s|\psi_s(t)\rangle .$$

In some cases,the operator F itself might be taken to be time-dependent:

$$F_s \equiv F_s(t).$$

It is frequently more convenient to formulate the theory so that the state vectors $|\psi_H\rangle$ which describe the system are time-independent while the operators $F_H(t)$ which describe the measurement of physical properties are time-dependent. Since only the expectation values of operators have physical meaning, this form of the theory (called the Heisenberg picture) will clearly be just as valid as the Schrödinger form provided we choose the time-dependence of the "Heisenberg" operators $F_H(t)$ so that

$$\langle \psi_s(t)|F_s(t)|\psi_s(t)\rangle = \langle \psi_H|F_H(t)|\psi_H\rangle .$$

To see what conditions are involved in this last relationship, we assume first that the Hamiltonian H_s in the Schrödinger picture is time-independent and that F_s is also - $F_s(t) = F_s(0) \equiv F_s$. It follows that

$$|\psi_s(t)\rangle = e^{-\frac{i}{\hbar} H_s t} |\psi_s(0)\rangle ,$$

$$\langle\psi_s(t)| = \langle\psi_s(0)| e^{\frac{i}{\hbar} H_s t} .$$

Furthermore, we choose the Heisenberg state vector $|\psi_H\rangle$ to be $|\psi_s(0)\rangle$, as we clearly may do if we wish. Then the relationship between expectation values becomes

$$\langle\psi_s(0)| e^{\frac{i}{\hbar} H_s t} F_s e^{-\frac{i}{\hbar} H_s t} |\psi_s(0)\rangle = \langle\psi_s(0)|F_H(t)|\psi_s(0)\rangle .$$

It follows immediately that

$$F_H(t) = e^{\frac{i}{\hbar} H_s t} F_s e^{-\frac{i}{\hbar} H_s t} .$$

In particular, we see that

$$H_H(t) = e^{\frac{i}{\hbar} H_s t} H_s e^{-\frac{i}{\hbar} H_s t} = H_s,$$

so the Heisenberg Hamiltonian is time-independent and equal to the Schrödinger Hamiltonian. Also, one finds by differentiation that

$$i\hbar \frac{d F_H(t)}{dt} = \left(-H e^{\frac{i}{\hbar} Ht}\right) F_s e^{-\frac{i}{\hbar} Ht} + e^{\frac{i}{\hbar} Ht} F_s \left(H e^{-\frac{i}{\hbar} Ht}\right)$$

$$= -H F_H(t) + F_H(t) H = [F_H(t), H] .$$

The operator $F_H(t)$ may then be characterized by the equation

$$i\hbar \frac{d F_H}{dt} = [F_H, H]$$

together with the boundary condition $F_H(0) = F_s$.

We shall use the Heisenberg picture exclusively for some time to come. The subscript H then does not need to be retained, since any operator which is used will be assumed to be a Heisenberg operator unless an explicit indication to the contrary is given.

2. Nonrelativistic Quantized Fields

a. Noninteracting Fields

In elementary quantum mechanics one most commonly works in terms of wave functions. This representation of the theory has several features which make it inconvenient in solid state applications. In the first place, wave functions for a crystal lattice would contain an intractably large number of spatial coordinates- of the order of 10^{22} or 10^{23}. In the second place, it is known that state vectors for systems containing more than one particle of the same kind must have certain (anti) symmetry properties; and these properties must be imposed a posteriori on the wave function instead of appearing as a natural result of the theory. Finally, it is difficult to describe by means of wave functions the behavior of systems in which particles are created or annihilated in the course of interaction in the system; but in order to properly describe, e.g., the electromagnetic interactions of solids and of impurities in solids, one must be able to consider processes in which photons are emitted or absorbed. It is easy to introduce a formalism, that of nonrelativistic quantized fields, which remedies all three of these difficulties.

One may go through all sorts of involved arguments to motivate the methods of so-called "second quantization." We shall give only a few simple indications of possible reasoning leading to the theory and then justify it at the end by the results. This is, in the long run, both the easiest and the most illuminating procedure. We can begin by noting that we usually find it convenient even in ordinary quantum mechanics to transfer all explicit time dependence to the operators of the theory (as just discussed). This suggests that it might be convenient, in general, to transfer all spatial dependence to the operators as well. Instead of representing an electron by a wave function $\Psi(\vec{r}, t)$, we assume that the electron is represented by an operator field $\psi(\vec{r}, t)$ in the sense that all operators describing measurements on a system of electrons can be formed from a suitable combination of ψ, its adjoint ψ^+, and the space and time derivatives of these two quantities. To find out how to form the various operators, we use a "correspondence principle" with ordinary wave mechanics. For instance, the expectation value of the Hamiltonian of a single particle in an external potential V $(\vec{r})$ would be, in terms of the wave function $\Psi(\vec{r}, t)$,

$$\langle H\rangle = \int d^3x\, \Psi^*(\vec{r}, t) \left[-\frac{\hbar^2}{2m} \nabla^2 + V(\vec{r})\right] \Psi(\vec{r}, t)$$

(Ψ a wave function).

We then take the Hamiltonian operator in our quantized field theory to be

$$H = \int d^3x\, \psi^+ (\vec{r}, t) \left[-\frac{\hbar^2}{2m} \nabla^2 + V(\vec{r})\right] \psi(\vec{r}, t)$$

(ψ an operator).

(An integration by parts transforms this to the equivalent expression

$$H = \int d^3x \left[\frac{\hbar^2}{2m} \vec{\nabla} \psi^+ \cdot \vec{\nabla} \psi + \psi^+ V\psi\right] = \int d^3x\, H(\vec{r}, t)$$

in which we may, if we wish, interpret the Hermitian operator $H(\vec{r}, t)$ as an energy <u>density</u> operator or <u>Hamiltonian</u> <u>density</u>. The quantity $H(\vec{r}, t)\, d^3x$ then corresponds to the physical process of measuring the energy of the system at time t in a volume element d^3x containing $\vec{r}$. A similar interpretation applies to other operator "densities" appearing as integrands.) To find the value of the energy of the system, with the usual statistical interpretation understood, we must now evaluate the expectation value of the operator H in the state of the system. Similarly, from

$$\langle \vec{P} \rangle = \int d^3 x\, \Psi^* (\vec{r}, t) \frac{\hbar}{i} \vec{\nabla}\, \Psi(\vec{r}, t)$$

(Ψ a wave function)

we deduce the expression

$$\vec{P} = \int d^3 x\, \psi^+ (\vec{r}, t) \frac{\hbar}{i} \vec{\nabla}\, \psi(\vec{r}, t)$$

$$= \frac{1}{2} \int d^3 x \left[\psi^+ \frac{\hbar}{i} \vec{\nabla} \psi - (\frac{\hbar}{i} \vec{\nabla} \psi^+) \psi\right]$$

(ψ an operator).

The procedure in general should now be clear. The name "second quantized" theory arises because the theory is obtained by replacing wave functions in "first quantized" physics by operators just as one replaced dynamical variables in classical theory by operators in order to arrive at the "first quantized" theory.

We assume that the equations of motion for our operators remain the same as in ordinary quantum mechanics. In particular,

$$i\hbar \frac{\partial \psi(\vec{r}, t)}{\partial t} = \left[\psi(\vec{r}, t), H\right].$$

Thus, to find the equations of motion, we must know the commutator of ψ with H. Since H is an integral of a function of ψ and its adjoint and derivatives, it is most convenient to specify commutation relations between the ψ's (and ψ^+'s) evaluated at different space-time points. The appropriate form of these commutation relations is easiest to find in the relativistic theory. Here we shall simply state the result and then show that using the commutation relations as a postulate leads one to agreement with the ordinary quantum theory in the well-known cases. The relations have different forms for the two types of particles found in nature.

1. When $\psi(\vec{r}, t)$ is the field operator for a system of <u>bosons</u>, then

$$\psi(\vec{r}, t)\,\psi^+(\vec{r}', t) - \psi^+(\vec{r}', t)\,\psi(\vec{r}, t) \equiv \left[\psi(\vec{r}, t), \psi^+(\vec{r}', t)\right]$$

$$= \delta(\vec{r} - \vec{r}'),$$

$$\left[\psi(\vec{r}, t), \psi(\vec{r}', t)\right] = \left[\psi^+(\vec{r}, t), \psi^+(\vec{r}', t)\right] = 0.$$

2. When $\psi(\vec{r}, t)$ is the field operator for a system of <u>fermions</u>, then

$$\psi(\vec{r}, t)\,\psi^+(\vec{r}', t) + \psi^+(\vec{r}', t)\,\psi(\vec{r}, t) \equiv \left[\psi(\vec{r}, t), \psi^+(\vec{r}', t)\right]_+$$

$$= \delta(\vec{r} - \vec{r}'),$$

$$\left[\psi(\vec{r}, t), \psi(\vec{r}', t)\right]_+ = \left[\psi^+(\vec{r}, t), \psi^+(\vec{r}', t)\right]_+ = 0.$$

Note that both operators appearing in the various (anti) commutators are evaluated at the same time t ; i. e., these are the equal-time commutation relations. We shall soon see that they not only lead to the correct equations of motion for the system, but that they also guarantee correct symmetry in all expressions appearing in the theory.

First let us verify the statement about the equations of motion. We shall consider the specific case where $\psi(\vec{r}, t)$ is the operator for a fermion field and the Hamiltonian H is

$$H = \int d^3 x' \, \psi^+ (\vec{r}', t') \left[- \frac{\hbar^2}{2m} \nabla'^2 + V(\vec{r}') \right] \psi(\vec{r}', t').$$

Then

$$i\hbar \frac{\partial \psi}{\partial t} = \left[\psi, H \right]$$

$$= \left[\psi(\vec{r}, t), \int d^3 x' \, \psi^+ (\vec{r}', t') \left[- \frac{\hbar^2}{2m} \nabla'^2 + V(\vec{r}') \right] \psi(\vec{r}', t') \right].$$

In general, we do not know the value of $\left[\psi(\vec{r}, t), \psi^+ (\vec{r}', t') \right]_+$, etc. But, since H is time-independent, we can take the time t' in the integrand to be =t without affecting things. This will allow us to use our equal-time commutation relations. We also make note of the following very useful relations:

$$\begin{aligned}
[A, BC] &= ABC - BCA \\
&= ABC + BAC - BAC - BCA \\
&= [A, B]_+ C - B [A, C]_+ , \\
[AB, C] &= ABC + ACB - ACB - CAB \\
&= A [B, C]_+ - [A, C]_+ B.
\end{aligned}$$

(The analogous relations

$$\begin{aligned}
[A, BC] &= ABC - BAC + BAC - BCA \\
&= [A, B] C + B [A, C] ,
\end{aligned}$$

$$[AB, C] = ABC - ACB + ACB - CAB$$
$$= A[B, C] + [A, C]B$$

for commutators are also frequently needed.) Using the first identity allows us to write

$$i\hbar \frac{\partial \psi(\vec{r}, t)}{\partial t} = \int d^3x' \left[\psi(\vec{r}, t), \psi^+(\vec{r'}, t)\right]_+ \cdot$$
$$\cdot \left[-\frac{\hbar^2}{2m} \nabla'^2 + V(\vec{r'})\right] \psi(\vec{r'}, t)$$

$$- \int d^3x' \, \psi^+ (\vec{r'}, t) \cdot$$
$$\cdot \left[\psi(\vec{r}, t), \left[-\frac{\hbar^2}{2m} \nabla'^2 + V(\vec{r'})\right] \psi(\vec{r'}, t)\right]_+ .$$

But

$$\left[\psi(\vec{r}, t), \psi^+(\vec{r'}, t)\right]_+ = \delta(\vec{r} - \vec{r'}),$$

and

$$\left[\psi(\vec{r}, t), \left[-\frac{\hbar^2}{2m} \nabla'^2 + V(\vec{r'})\right] \psi(r', t)\right]_+$$
$$= \left[-\frac{\hbar^2}{2m} \nabla'^2 + V(\vec{r'})\right] \left[\psi(\vec{r}, t), \psi(\vec{r'}, t)\right]_+ = 0.$$

Thus, one finally sees that

$$i\hbar \frac{\partial \psi(\vec{r}, t)}{\partial t} = \int d^3x' \, \delta(\vec{r} - \vec{r'}) \left[-\frac{\hbar^2}{2m} \nabla'^2 + V(\vec{r'})\right] \psi(\vec{r'}, t)$$
$$= \left[-\frac{\hbar^2}{2m} \nabla^2 + V(\vec{r})\right] \psi(\vec{r}, t).$$

That is, ψ satisfies the same equation, even though an operator, that the wave function for a single particle satisfies. However, there are very important differences between the two cases. For one thing, there is only one ψ (up to unitary equivalences) which satisfies the equations of motion and the relations

$$[\psi(\vec{r}, t), \psi^+(\vec{r}', t)]_+ = \delta(\vec{r} - \vec{r}'), \quad [\psi(\vec{r}, t), \psi(\vec{r}', t)]_+ = 0,$$

as well as permitting the existence of a vacuum state to be introduced below, while an infinite set of independent wave-function solutions of the Schrödinger equation exist. Furthermore, in the more general case (which we shall soon consider) where the particles described by the field interact with one another (e.g., when the particles are charged), the field operator ψ no longer obeys this simple one-particle equation, but rather a much more complicated nonlinear integrodifferential equation.

To make further progress with our theory, we need to introduce the concept which has just been mentioned of a vacuum state. We suppose that there exists a state (which may be interpreted physically as having no particles present) which is a zero-momentum state and which is also an energy eigenstate with eigenvalue zero. This state $|0\rangle$, for which

$$H|0\rangle = 0, \quad \vec{P}|0\rangle = 0,$$

is taken to be normalized and unique (up to a numerical factor of modulus one). Since

$$H = \int d^3x\, \psi^+(\vec{r}, t) \left[-\frac{\hbar^2}{2m} \nabla^2 + V(\vec{r}) \right] \psi(\vec{r}, t),$$

$$\vec{P} = \int d^3x\, \psi^+(\vec{r}, t) \frac{\hbar}{i} \vec{\nabla} \psi(r, t),$$

the simplest way to satisfy these requirements is to demand that

$$\psi(\vec{r}, t)|0\rangle = 0, \quad \text{all } \vec{r}, t.$$

We say that $\psi(\vec{r}, t)$ annihilates the vacuum state. To give an interpretation to our operator fields and to their relationship to the vacuum state, we may now proceed as follows. We introduce an operator

$$N = \int d^3x \; \psi^+(\vec{r}, t)\, \psi(\vec{r}, t)$$

whose properties are as follows:

1. $N^+ = N$ (obviously);

2. $\frac{dN}{dt} = 0$. In fact, if we choose the same time t in the integrands for both N and H and use the abbreviation $K(\vec{r}) = -\frac{h^2}{2m}\nabla^2 + V(\vec{r})$, then we see that

$$\begin{aligned}
[N, H] &= \int d^3x\, d^3x' \left[\psi^+(\vec{r}', t)\, \psi(\vec{r}', t),\ \psi^+(\vec{r}, t)\, K(\vec{r})\, \psi(\vec{r}, t)\right] \\
&= \int d^3x\, d^3x' \Big\{\psi^+(\vec{r}', t) \left[\psi(\vec{r}', t),\ \psi^+(\vec{r}, t)\, K(\vec{r})\, \psi(\vec{r}, t)\right] \\
&\qquad + \left[\psi^+(\vec{r}', t),\ \psi^+(\vec{r}, t)\, K(\vec{r})\, \psi(\vec{r}, t)\right] \psi(\vec{r}', t)\Big\} \\
&= \int d^3x\, d^3x' \Big\{\psi^+(\vec{r}', t) \left[\psi(\vec{r}', t),\ \psi^+(r, t)\right]_\pm K(\vec{r})\, \psi(\vec{r}, t) \\
&\qquad \mp \psi^+(\vec{r}'\ t)\, \psi^+(\vec{r}, t) \left[\psi(\vec{r}', t),\ K(\vec{r})\, \psi(\vec{r}, t)\right]_\pm \\
&\qquad + \left[\psi^+(\vec{r}', t),\ \psi^+(\vec{r}, t)\right]_\pm K(\vec{r})\, \psi(\vec{r}, t)\, \psi(\vec{r}', t) \\
&\qquad \mp \psi^+(\vec{r}, t) \left[\psi^+(\vec{r}', t),\ K(\vec{r})\, \psi(\vec{r}, t)\right]_\pm \psi(\vec{r}', t)\Big\} \\
&= \int d^3x\, d^3x' \Big\{\delta(\vec{r} - \vec{r}')\, \psi^+(\vec{r}', t) \left[-\frac{\hbar^2}{2m}\nabla^2 + V(\vec{r})\right] \psi(\vec{r}, t) \\
&\qquad - \psi^+(\vec{r}, t)\, \psi(\vec{r}', t) \left[-\frac{\hbar^2}{2m}\nabla^2 + V(\vec{r})\right] \delta(\vec{r} - \vec{r}')\Big\} \\
&= \int d^3x' \Big\{\psi^+(\vec{r}', t) \left[-\frac{\hbar^2}{2m}\nabla'^2 + V(\vec{r}')\right] \psi(\vec{r}', t) \\
&\qquad - \left[\left(-\frac{\hbar^2}{2m}\nabla'^2 + V(\vec{r}')\right) \psi^+(\vec{r}', t)\right] \psi(\vec{r}', t)\Big\} = 0,
\end{aligned}$$

since ∇^2 is Hermitian.

3. Finally,

$$[\psi(\vec{r}, t), N] = \int d^3x' \, [\psi(\vec{r}, t), \psi^+(\vec{r}', t)\, \psi(\vec{r}', t)]$$

$$= \int d^3x' \left\{ [\psi(\vec{r}, t), \psi^+(\vec{r}', t)]_{\pm} \, \psi(\vec{r}', t) \right.$$

$$\left. \mp \psi^+(\vec{r}', t) \, [\psi(\vec{r}, t), \psi(\vec{r}', t)]_{\pm} \right\}$$

$$= \int d^3x' \, \delta(\vec{r} - \vec{r}') \, \psi(\vec{r}', t) = \psi(\vec{r}, t).$$

Here the cases where ψ describes a boson field and those where ψ describes a fermion field have been considered simultaneously by introducing the notation $[\ ,\ ]_-$ for the commutator. Either the upper or the lower sign should be taken throughout, with the commutator being chosen for boson operators and the anticommutator for fermion operators. The result is the same in either case. We note that by taking the adjoint of the relation

$$[\psi(\vec{r}, t), N] = \psi(\vec{r}, t),$$

we find

$$[\psi^+(\vec{r}, t), N] = -\psi^+(\vec{r}, t).$$

By a double application of these relations, we find that

$$[\psi(\vec{r}_1, t_1) \; \psi(\vec{r}_2, t_2), N] =$$

$$= \psi(\vec{r}_1, t_1) \, [\psi(\vec{r}_2, t_2), N] + [\psi(\vec{r}_1, t_1), N] \, \psi(\vec{r}_2, t_2)$$

$$= 2\psi(\vec{r}_1, t_1) \, \psi(\vec{r}_2, t_2),$$

and in general one may show by induction that

$$[\psi(\vec{r}_1, t_1) \ldots \psi(\vec{r}_n, t_n), N] = n\psi(\vec{r}_1, t_1) \ldots \psi(\vec{r}_n, t_n),$$

$$[\psi^+(\vec{r}_1, t_1) \ldots \psi^+(\vec{r}_n, t_n), N] = -n\psi^+(\vec{r}_1, t_1) \ldots \psi^+(\vec{r}_n, t_n).$$

These commutation relations now make it possible to give an interpretation of the significance of the operator N and, in turn, of the operators ψ and ψ^+. We note that since N is Hermitian it may be regarded as an operator corresponding to the measurement of some physical property of the system. To see what this property is, we merely need to notice first that

$$N|O\rangle = 0 = 0|O\rangle$$

(since ψ stands to the right in $N = \int d^3x\, \psi^+(\vec{r}, t)\, \psi(\vec{r}, t)$ and $\psi(\vec{r}, t)|0\rangle = 0$); next, that if $C(\vec{r})$ is any integrable function of r and $|C_1, t\rangle$ is the state vector

$$|C_1, t\rangle = \int d^3x\, C(\vec{r})\, \psi^+(\vec{r}, t)\, |0\rangle$$

then

$$\begin{aligned} N\,|C_1, t\rangle &= \int d^3x\, C(\vec{r}) \left\{ \left[N, \psi^+(\vec{r}, t)\right] + \psi^+(\vec{r}, t)\, N \right\} |0\rangle \\ &= \int d^3x\, C(\vec{r})\, \psi^+(\vec{r}, t)\, |0\rangle \\ &= 1 \cdot |C_1, t\rangle ; \end{aligned}$$

and in general, if $C(\vec{r}_1, \ldots, \vec{r}_n)$ is any integrable function of its n arguments and $|C_n, t\rangle$ is the state vector

$$|C_n, t\rangle = \int d^3x_1 \ldots d^3x_n\, C(\vec{r}_1, \ldots, \vec{r}_n)\, \psi^+(\vec{r}_1, t) \ldots \psi^+(\vec{r}_n, t)\, |0\rangle$$

then

$$\begin{aligned} N\,|C_n, t\rangle &= \int d^3x_1 \ldots d^3x_n\, C(\vec{r}_1, \ldots, \vec{r}_n) \\ &\quad \times \Big\{ \left[N, \psi^+(\vec{r}_1, t) \ldots \psi^+(\vec{r}_n, t)\right] \\ &\quad + \psi^+(\vec{r}_1, t) \ldots \psi^+(\vec{r}_n, t)\, N \Big\} |0\rangle \\ &= n \int d^3x_1 \ldots d^3x_n\, C(\vec{r}_1, \ldots, \vec{r}_n) \\ &\quad \psi^+(\vec{r}_1, t) \ldots \psi^+(\vec{r}_n, t)\, |0\rangle \\ &= n\,|C_n, t\rangle . \end{aligned}$$

These results indicate that possibly we should think of N as an operator representing the determination of the number of particles present. It would then follow that when we apply the operator $\psi^+(\vec{r}, t)$ to a state with a given number of particles present we create a state with an additional particle present. To check the validity of this interpretation we need to find the connection between a state which, for instance, might be of the form $\int d^3x\, C(\vec{r})\, \psi^+(\vec{r}, t)\, |0\rangle$ and the quantities in ordinary quantum mechanics whose interpretation we know. We may do this by trying to choose a $C(\vec{r})$ such that the above state is an eigenstate of H and seeing what condition this leads to; i. e., we require that

$$H\int d^3x\, C(\vec{r})\, \psi^+(\vec{r}, t)\, |0\rangle = E\int d^3x\, C(\vec{r})\, \psi^+(\vec{r}, t)\, |0\rangle$$

for some (real) number E. But we have found that

$$[\psi(\vec{r}, t),\ H] = \left[-\frac{\hbar^2}{2m}\nabla^2 + V(\vec{r})\right] \psi(\vec{r}, t),$$

and taking the adjoint of this equation shows that

$$[H,\ \psi^+(\vec{r}, t)] = \left[-\frac{\hbar^2}{2m}\nabla^2 + V(\vec{r})\right] \psi^+(\vec{r}, t).$$

Then

$$H\int d^3x\, C(\vec{r})\, \psi^+(\vec{r}, t)\, |0\rangle$$

$$= \int d^3x\, C(\vec{r}) \left\{[H,\ \psi^+(\vec{r}, t)] + \psi^+(\vec{r}, t)\, H\right\} |0\rangle$$

$$= \int d^3x\, C(\vec{r}) \left[-\frac{\hbar^2}{2m}\nabla^2 + V(\vec{r})\right] \psi^+(\vec{r}, t)\, |0\rangle$$

$$= \int d^3x \left\{\left[-\frac{\hbar^2}{2m}\nabla^2 + V(\vec{r})\right] C(\vec{r})\right\} \psi^+(\vec{r}, t)\, |0\rangle$$

(by an integration by parts)

$$= E\int d^3x\, C(\vec{r})\, \psi^+(\vec{r}, t)\, |0\rangle.$$

That is, $C(\vec{r})$ must satisfy the usual one-particle Schrödinger eigenvalue equation

$$\left[-\frac{\hbar^2}{2m}\nabla^2 + V(\vec{r})\right] C(\vec{r}) = E\, C(\vec{r}),$$

and E must be one of the one-particle energy eigenvalues. Similarly, one may show that if

$$H\int d^3x_1\, d^3x_2\; C(\vec{r}_1, \vec{r}_2)\,\psi^+(\vec{r}_1, t)\,\psi^+(\vec{r}_2, t)\,|0\rangle$$

$$= E'\int d^3x_1\, d^3x_2\; C(\vec{r}_1, \vec{r}_2)\,\psi^+(\vec{r}_1, t)\,\psi^+(\vec{r}_2, t)\,|0\rangle,$$

then $C(\vec{r}_1, \vec{r}_2)$ is a solution of the two-particle eigenvalue equation and E' is a two-particle energy eigenvalue (we shall give the proof of this later), and so on for $C(\vec{r}_1, \ldots, \vec{r}_n)$ for any n. This result not only shows that our interpretation of the operator N and the states $|C_n, t\rangle$ is justified, but at the same time shows that our single operator field $\psi(\vec{r}, t)$ contains all the information necessary to describe systems containing any number of particles. This was the first claim made for the second-quantized formalism at the beginning of our discussion.

At this point we might just as well discuss the second point mentioned there, the matter of the automatic (anti) symmetrization of quantities which arise in quantum field theory. It is easiest to see this effect in the n-particle state vectors

$$|C_n, t\rangle = \int d^3x_1\, d^3x_2 \ldots d^3x_n\; C(\vec{r}_1, \ldots, \vec{r}_n)\,\cdot$$

$$\cdot\, \psi^+(\vec{r}_1, t) \ldots \psi^+(\vec{r}_n, t)\,|0\rangle\,.$$

Note that if ψ describes a fermion field then the state vector

$$\psi^+(\vec{r}_1, t) \ldots \psi^+(\vec{r}_n, t)\,|0\rangle$$

is antisymmetric under the interchange of two of the $\vec{r}$'s, since

$$\left[\psi^+(\vec{r}, t), \psi^+(\vec{r}\,', t)\right]_+ = 0 = \psi^+(\vec{r}, t)\,\psi^+(\vec{r}\,', t) + \psi^+(\vec{r}\,', t)\,\psi^+(\vec{r}, t).$$

For instance, by use of this relation we can see that

$$\psi^+(\vec{r}_2, t)\,\psi^+(\vec{r}_1, t) \ldots \psi^+(\vec{r}_n, t)\,|0\rangle = -\psi^+(\vec{r}_1, t)\,\psi^+(\vec{r}_2, t) \ldots \psi^+(\vec{r}_n, t)\,|0\rangle,$$

and similarly for the interchange of other pairs of arguments. It follows that only the part of $C(\vec{r}_1, \ldots, \vec{r}_n)$ which is antisymmetric under interchange of any two of its arguments will actually contribute to the integral for the state vector

$$|C_n, t\rangle = \int d^3 x_1 \ldots d^3 x_n \, C(\vec{r}_1, \ldots \vec{r}_n) \, \psi^+(\vec{r}_1, t) \ldots \psi^+(\vec{r}_n, t) \, |0\rangle ,$$

and therefore only this part of C has physical significance - i. e., we should think of C as being antisymmetric under interchange of any two of its arguments from the start. Similarly one can see immediately that if ψ describes a boson field, so that

$$[\psi^+(\vec{r}, t), \psi^+(\vec{r}\,', t)] = 0 = \psi^+(\vec{r}, t) \psi^+(\vec{r}\,', t) - \psi^+(\vec{r}\,', t) \psi^+(\vec{r}, t),$$

then only the part of $C(\vec{r}_1, \ldots, \vec{r}_n)$ which is <u>symmetric</u> under interchange of any two arguments has physical significance. Our introduction of equal-time commutation or anticommutation relations thus automatically takes care of the "statistics" of the theory for us without further attention on our part. Some additional remarks about the implications of the (anti) commutation relations will be made later.

We can obtain further information about the nature of the operators ψ, ψ^+ by considering the one-particle state $|\vec{r}_0, t\rangle$ in which we take the function $C(\vec{r})$ to be $\delta(\vec{r} - \vec{r}_0)$:

$$|\vec{r}_0, t\rangle = \int d^3 x \, \delta(\vec{r} - \vec{r}_0) \psi^+(\vec{r}, t) \, |0\rangle = \psi^+(\vec{r}_0, t) \, |0\rangle .$$

We know that this is a one-particle state. To find out what <u>sort</u> of state it is, we introduce the position operator

$$\vec{R}(t) = \int d^3 x \, \psi^+(\vec{r}, t) \, \vec{r} \, \psi(\vec{r}, t) = \vec{R}(t)^+.$$

The form of this operator has been obtained by our "correspondence principle". We can substantiate this form further by observing that

$$[P_\alpha, R_\beta] = \left[\int d^3 x \psi^+(\vec{r}, t) \frac{\hbar}{i} \partial_\alpha \psi(\vec{r}, t), \int d^3 x' \psi^+(\vec{r}\,', t) x'_\beta \, \psi(\vec{r}\,', t)\right]$$

$$= \int d^3 x \, d^3 x' \{\psi^+(\vec{r}, t) \frac{\hbar}{i} \partial_\alpha [\psi(\vec{r}, t), \psi^+(\vec{r}\,', t) \, x'_\beta \, \psi(\vec{r}\,', t)]$$

$$+ [\psi^+(\vec{r}, t), \psi^+(\vec{r}\,', t) x'_\beta \psi(\vec{r}\,', t)] \frac{\hbar}{i} \partial_\alpha \, \psi(\vec{r}, t)\}$$

$$= \int d^3x\, d^3x' \Big\{ \psi^+(\vec{r}, t) \left[\frac{\hbar}{i} \partial_\alpha \left[\psi(\vec{r}, t), \psi^+(\vec{r}\,', t) \right]_\pm \right] x'_\beta\, \psi(\vec{r}\,', t)$$

$$\mp \psi^+(\vec{r}\,', t)\, x'_\beta \left[\psi^+(\vec{r}, t), \psi(\vec{r}\,', t) \right]_\pm \frac{\hbar}{i} \partial_\alpha\, \psi(\vec{r}, t) \Big\}$$

(where we have not bothered to write down vanishing terms)

$$= \int d^3x\, d^3x' \Big\{ \left[- \frac{\hbar}{i} \partial_\alpha\, \psi^+(\vec{r}, t) \right] \delta(\vec{r} - \vec{r}\,')\, x'_\beta\, \psi(\vec{r}\,', t)$$

$$- \psi^+(\vec{r}\,', t)\, x'_\beta\ \delta(\vec{r} - \vec{r}\,')\, \frac{\hbar}{i} \partial_\alpha\, \psi(\vec{r}, t) \Big\}$$

(performing an integration by parts in the first term as well as using the equal-time commutation relations)

$$= \int d^3 x \Big\{ \psi^+(\vec{r}, t)\, \frac{\hbar}{i} \partial_\alpha \left[x_\beta\, \psi(\vec{r}, t) \right]$$

$$- \psi^+(\vec{r}, t)\, x_\beta\, \frac{\hbar}{i} \partial_\alpha\, \psi(\vec{r}, t) \Big\}$$

(integrating over $\vec{r}\,'$ and then integrating by parts in the first term)

$$= \frac{\hbar}{i} \delta_{\alpha\beta} \int d^3 x\ \psi^+(\vec{r}, t)\, \psi(\vec{r}, t) = \frac{\hbar}{i} \delta_{\alpha\beta} N.$$

That is,

$$\left[P_\alpha(t), R_\beta(t) \right] = \frac{\hbar}{i} \delta_{\alpha\beta} N.$$

Since $N = 1$ for one-particle states, these are just the usual p-q commutation relations in the case where the theory should correspond with ordinary quantum mechanics. To see the effect of $\vec{R}$ when applied to our states, we note that

$$\left[\psi(\vec{r}, t), \vec{R}(t) \right] = \int d^3 x' \left[\psi(\vec{r}, t), \psi^+(\vec{r}\,', t)\, \vec{r}\,'\, \psi(\vec{r}\,', t) \right]$$

$$= \int d^3 x'\ \delta(\vec{r} - \vec{r}\,')\, \vec{r}\,'\, \psi(\vec{r}\,', t) = \vec{r}\, \psi(\vec{r}, t),$$

and

$$\left[\vec{R}(t), \psi^+(\vec{r},t)\right] = \vec{r}\,\psi^+(\vec{r},t).$$

Then for one of our states $|\vec{r}_o, t\rangle = \psi^+(\vec{r}_o, t)\,|0\rangle$ we find

$$\vec{R}(t)\,|\vec{r}_o, t\rangle = \left[\vec{R}(t), \psi^+(\vec{r}_o, t)\right]|0\rangle + \psi^+(\vec{r}_o, t)\,\vec{R}(t)\,|0\rangle$$

$$= \vec{r}_o\ \psi^+(\vec{r}_o, t)\,|0\rangle = \vec{r}_o\,|\vec{r}_o, t\rangle$$

(since clearly $\vec{R}(t)\,|0\rangle = 0$). In other words, $\psi^+(\vec{r},t)$ creates a particle at the position $\vec{r}$ at time t. On the basis of ordinary quantum mechanics we would expect such states to be nonnormalizable, and in fact we see that

$$\langle \vec{r}', t|\vec{r}, t\rangle = \langle 0|\,\psi(\vec{r}', t)\,\psi^+(\vec{r}, t)\,|0\rangle$$

$$= \langle 0|\left[\mp\psi^+(\vec{r},t)\,\psi(\vec{r}',t) + \delta(\vec{r}-\vec{r}')\right]|0\rangle = \delta(\vec{r}-\vec{r}').$$

Thus

$$\langle \vec{r}', t|\vec{r}, t\rangle = \begin{cases} 0, & \vec{r}' \neq \vec{r} \\ \delta(0) = \infty, & \vec{r}' = \vec{r}. \end{cases}$$

Finally, we note that just as $\psi^+(\vec{r}, t)$ creates a particle at the position $\vec{r}$ at time t, its adjoint $\psi(\vec{r}, t)$ destroys a particle at the position $\vec{r}$ at time t. To see this most clearly, we may simply note that the state vector

$$\int d^3x'\ C(\vec{r}')\,\psi^+(\vec{r}', t)\,|0\rangle$$

may be thought of as the expansion of a general one-particle state as a sum of one-particle states each of which has a particle present at a given point. Applying $\psi(\vec{r}, t)$ to this expression gives the result

$$\int d^3x'\ C(\vec{r}')\left\{\left[\psi(\vec{r},t), \psi^+(r',t)\right]_\pm \mp \psi^+(\vec{r}',t)\,\psi(\vec{r},t)\right\}|0\rangle = C(\vec{r})\,|0\rangle\,.$$

$C(\vec{r})$ was the coefficient of our state with one particle at the point $\vec{r}$ in the original state; it is now the coefficient of the vacuum state, which shows that the particle originally present at point $\vec{r}$ has been annihilated. The rest of the original state vector (the sum of $C(\vec{r}\,')\ \psi^+(\vec{r}\,', t)\ |0\rangle$ for $\vec{r}\,' \neq \vec{r}$) did not have a particle present at the point $\vec{r}$. It was thus a vacuum state as far as the operator $\psi(\vec{r}, t)$ was concerned, and so has been completely eradicated.

b. The Theory for Interacting Particles

So far all our discussion involving the dynamics of our system has assumed that the Hamiltonian was of the form

$$H = \int d^3 x\ \psi^+(\vec{r}, t) \left[- \frac{\hbar^2}{2m} \nabla^2 + V(\vec{r}) \right] \psi(\vec{r}, t).$$

That is, the only interaction of the system is with an external field described by the potential $V(\vec{r})$. Now let us suppose that the particles described by the field exert forces on one another. We shall suppose these forces to be conservative two-body forces. By two-body forces we mean that the forces act between pairs of particles, and that the force for a given pair of particles is independent of the presence of other particles. Our forces can then be described by a potential function which depends on the coordinates of two particles. A particular example of this type is the case of the electrostatic forces between two charged particles in the nonrelativistic limit. Since this electrostatic force is of great significance in solid state theory, we might as well use it as an example to see what sort of interaction term we must add to our Hamiltonian. It is known from electromagnetic theory that the potential energy due to the electrostatic interaction of a charge distribution of charge density ρ with itself is

$$\tfrac{1}{2} \int d^3 x\, d^3 x' \ \frac{\rho(\vec{r})\ \rho(\vec{r}\,')}{|\vec{r} - \vec{r}\,'|} .$$

In quantum mechanics $\rho(\vec{r})$ is $e\,\Psi^*(\vec{r}, t)\,\Psi(\vec{r}, t)$ in terms of wave functions, so the interaction energy is

$$\tfrac{1}{2} \int d^3 x\, d^3 x' \ \frac{e^2\, \Psi^*(\vec{r}, t)\ \Psi(\vec{r}, t)\ \Psi^*(\vec{r}\,', t)\ \Psi(\vec{r}\,', t)}{|\vec{r} - \vec{r}\,'|} .$$

To make the transition to our general quantum theory of interacting particles, we replace $e^2/|\vec{r} - \vec{r}'|$ by any two-body potential $v(\vec{r}', \vec{r})$ and then replace the wave functions by operators to arrive at the Hamiltonian

$$H = \int d^3x\, \psi^+(\vec{r}, t)\left[-\frac{\hbar^2}{2m} \nabla^2 + V(\vec{r})\right] \psi(\vec{r}', t)$$

$$+ \frac{1}{2}\int d^3x\, d^3x'\, \psi^+(\vec{r}, t)\, \psi^+(\vec{r}', t)\, v(\vec{r}', \vec{r})\, \psi(\vec{r}', t)\, \psi(\vec{r}, t).$$

It will be noted that we have slightly altered the order of factors in the interaction term. This was done to prevent the appearance of meaningless infinite "self-energy" terms due to the interaction of a particle with itself. One can easily see how such terms would arise by changing the order shown, using the commutation relations.

Let us obtain the equation of motion for ψ in this interacting case, using the same equal-time commutation relations as before. We know the commutator of ψ with the kinetic energy and external potential terms already, so we only need to compute the commutator of ψ with the interaction term. We see that

$$\left[\psi(\vec{r}_0, t),\ \psi^+(\vec{r}, t)\, \psi^+(\vec{r}', t)\, \psi(\vec{r}', t)\, \psi(\vec{r}, t)\right]$$

$$= \left[\psi(\vec{r}_0, t),\ \psi^+(\vec{r}, t)\, \psi^+(\vec{r}', t)\right]\psi(\vec{r}', t)\, \psi(\vec{r}, t)$$

$$= \left\{ \left[\psi(\vec{r}_0, t),\ \psi^+(\vec{r}, t)\right]_{\pm}\ \psi^+(\vec{r}', t)\right.$$

$$\left. \mp\ \psi^+(\vec{r}, t)\left[\psi(\vec{r}_0, t),\ \psi^+(\vec{r}', t)\right]_{\pm}\right\}\psi(\vec{r}', t)\, \psi(\vec{r}, t)$$

$$= \left[\delta(\vec{r}_0 - \vec{r})\, \psi^+(\vec{r}', t) \mp \delta(\vec{r}_0 - \vec{r}')\, \psi^+(\vec{r}, t)\right]\psi(\vec{r}', t)\, \psi(\vec{r}, t).$$

Then

$$\left[\psi(\vec{r}_0, t), H_{int}\right] = \frac{1}{2}\int d^3x\, d^3x'\, v(\vec{r}', \vec{r})\left[\psi(\vec{r}_0, t),\ \psi^+(\vec{r}, t)\psi^+(\vec{r}', t)\psi(\vec{r}', t)\psi(\vec{r}, t)\right]$$

$$= \frac{1}{2}\int d^3x\, v(\vec{r}_0, \vec{r})\left[\psi^+(\vec{r}, t)\, \psi(\vec{r}, t)\, \psi(\vec{r}_0, t) \mp \psi^+(\vec{r}, t)\, \psi(\vec{r}_0, t)\, \psi(\vec{r}, t)\right]$$

$$= \left[\int d^3x\, \psi^+(\vec{r}, t)\, \psi(\vec{r}, t)\, v(\vec{r}, \vec{r}_0)\right]\psi(\vec{r}_0, t).$$

We have explicitly made use of the fact that v can be considered a symmetric function of its arguments (since the function $\psi^+(\vec{r}, t)\,\psi^+(\vec{r}', t)\,\psi(\vec{r}', t)\,\psi(\vec{r}, t)$ which it multiplies in H is symmetric in $\vec{r}$ and $\vec{r}'$). We thus obtain the final result:

$$i\hbar \frac{\partial \psi(\vec{r}, t)}{\partial t} = \left[\psi(\vec{r}, t), H\right]$$

$$= \left[-\frac{\hbar^2}{2m}\nabla^2 + V(\vec{r}) + \int d^3x'\, \psi^+(\vec{r}', t)\,\psi(\vec{r}', t)\, v(\vec{r}', \vec{r})\right]\psi(\vec{r}, t).$$

This is the nonlinear integrodifferential equation which was promised earlier. Taking the adjoint yields the relation

$$-i\hbar \frac{\partial \psi^+(\vec{r}, t)}{\partial t} = \left[H, \psi^+(\vec{r}, t)\right]$$

$$= \left[-\frac{\hbar^2}{2m}\nabla^2 + V(\vec{r})\right]\psi^+(\vec{r}, t) + \psi^+(\vec{r}, t)\int d^3x'\, \psi^+(\vec{r}', t)\,\psi(\vec{r}', t)\, v(\vec{r}, \vec{r}').$$

($v(\vec{r}, \vec{r}')$ must clearly be real if H is to be Hermitian.)

To show that our interacting field theory actually is equivalent to the more familiar representation in terms of wave functions, let us try to determine the function $C(\vec{r}_1, \vec{r}_2)$ which makes

$$|C_2, t\rangle = \int d^3x_1\, d^3x_2\, C(\vec{r}_1, \vec{r}_2)\, \psi^+(\vec{r}_1, t)\, \psi^+(\vec{r}_2, t)\, |0\rangle$$

an eigenstate of H. We must calculate the quantity

$$H\psi^+(\vec{r}_1)\,\psi^+(\vec{r}_2)\,|0\rangle = \left[H, \psi^+(\vec{r}_1)\,\psi^+(\vec{r}_2)\right]|0\rangle$$

(where the argument t is understood and the relation $H|0\rangle = 0$ has been used)

$$= \left[H, \psi^+(\vec{r}_1)\right]\psi^+(\vec{r}_2)\,|0\rangle + \psi^+(\vec{r}_1)\left[H, \psi^+(\vec{r}_2)\right]|0\rangle$$

$$= \left\{\left[-\frac{\hbar^2}{2m}\nabla_1^2 + V(\vec{r}_1)\right]\psi^+(\vec{r}_1) + \psi^+(\vec{r}_1)\int d^3x'\, \psi^+(\vec{r}')\,\psi(\vec{r}')\, v(\vec{r}_1, \vec{r}')\right\}\psi^+(\vec{r}_2)\,|0\rangle$$

$$+ \psi^+(\vec{r}_1)\left[-\frac{\hbar^2}{2m}\nabla_2^2 + V(\vec{r}_2)\right]\psi^+(\vec{r}_2)\,|0\rangle,$$

where we have not written the integral term from $\left[H, \psi^+(\vec{r}_2)\right]$ because it merely annihilates the vacuum state. Now

$$\psi^+(\vec{r}_1)\left[\int d^3x'\, \psi^+(\vec{r}')\, \psi(\vec{r}')\, v(\vec{r}_1, \vec{r}')\right] \psi^+(\vec{r}_2)\, |0\rangle$$

$$= \psi^+(\vec{r}_1)\left\{\int d^3x'\, \psi^+(\vec{r}')\left[\mp\psi^+(\vec{r}_2)\, \psi(\vec{r}') + \delta(\vec{r}_2 - \vec{r}')\right] v(\vec{r}_1, \vec{r}')\right\} |0\rangle$$

$$= v(\vec{r}_1, \vec{r}_2)\, \psi^+(\vec{r}_1)\, \psi^+(\vec{r}_2)\, |0\rangle.$$

Thus we find

$$H\psi^+(\vec{r}_1)\psi^+(\vec{r}_2)\, |0\rangle =$$

$$= \left[-\frac{\hbar^2}{2m}\nabla_1^2 - \frac{\hbar^2}{2m}\nabla_2^2 + V(\vec{r}_1) + V(\vec{r}_2) + v(\vec{r}_1, \vec{r}_2)\right]\psi^+(\vec{r}_1)\, \psi^+(\vec{r}_2)\, |0\rangle\ ;$$

so

$$H\int d^3x_1\, d^3x_2\, C(\vec{r}_1, \vec{r}_2)\, \psi^+(\vec{r}_1)\, \psi^+(\vec{r}_2)\, |0\rangle$$

$$= E\int d^3x_1\, d^3x_2\, C(\vec{r}_1, \vec{r}_2)\, \psi^+(\vec{r}_1)\, \psi^+(\vec{r}_2)\, |0\rangle$$

if

$$\left[-\frac{\hbar^2}{2m}\nabla_1^2 - \frac{\hbar^2}{2m}\nabla_2^2 + V(\vec{r}_1) + V(\vec{r}_2) + v(\vec{r}_1, \vec{r}_2)\right]C(\vec{r}_1, \vec{r}_2) = E\, C(\vec{r}_1, \vec{r}_2).$$

This is just the Schrödinger eigenvalue equation for a wavefunction describing two identical particles which interact both with an external potential $V(\vec{r})$ and with each other (via $v(\vec{r}, \vec{r}')$). Furthermore, the theory implies just as before that only the (anti) symmetrized part of $C(\vec{r}_1, \vec{r}_2)$ contributes to the state vector.

It is easy to see that even in this interacting-particle case the number operator

$$N = \int d^3x\, \psi^+(\vec{r}, t)\, \psi(\vec{r}, t)$$

commutes with the Hamiltonian. In this connection we only need to verify that

$$[N, H_{int}] \equiv \left[\int d^3x\, \psi^+(\vec{r})\psi(\vec{r}),\ \tfrac{1}{2}\int d^3x_1\, d^3x_2\, \psi^+(\vec{r}_1)\psi^+(\vec{r}_2)v(\vec{r}_2, \vec{r}_1)\psi(\vec{r}_2)\psi(\vec{r}_1)\right] = 0,$$

since we have already seen that N commutes with the rest of the Hamiltonian. In the commutator above we suppose that all the ψ's are evaluated at the same time t, which is not explicitly written. The expression of interest may be rewritten (aside from a factor $\frac{1}{2}$) as

$$\int d^3x\, d^3x_1\, d^3x_2 \Big\{ [\psi^+(\vec{r})\, \psi(\vec{r}),\ \psi^+(\vec{r}_1)\, \psi^+(\vec{r}_2)]\ \psi(\vec{r}_2)\, \psi(\vec{r}_1)$$

$$+\ \psi^+(\vec{r}_1)\, \psi^+(\vec{r}_2)\ [\psi^+(\vec{r})\, \psi(\vec{r}),\ \psi(\vec{r}_2)\, \psi(\vec{r}_1)]\Big\}\ v(\vec{r}_2, \vec{r}_1).$$

Now

$$[\psi^+(\vec{r})\, \psi(\vec{r}),\ \psi^+(\vec{r}_1)\, \psi^+(\vec{r}_2)] = \psi^+(\vec{r})\ [\psi(\vec{r}),\ \psi^+(\vec{r}_1)\, \psi^+(\vec{r}_2)]$$

$$= \psi^+(\vec{r})\Big\{ [\psi(\vec{r}),\ \psi^+(r_1)]_\pm\ \psi^+(\vec{r}_2) \mp \psi^+(\vec{r}_1)\ [\psi(\vec{r}),\ \psi^+(\vec{r}_2)]_\pm \Big\}$$

$$= \psi^+(\vec{r})\, \psi^+(\vec{r}_2)\, \delta(\vec{r}-\vec{r}_1) \mp \psi^+(\vec{r})\, \psi^+(\vec{r}_1)\, \delta(\vec{r}-\vec{r}_2)$$

$$= \psi^+(\vec{r})\, \psi^+(\vec{r}_2)\, \delta(\vec{r}-\vec{r}_1) + \psi^+(\vec{r}_1)\, \psi^+(\vec{r})\, \delta(\vec{r}-\vec{r}_2).$$

Similarly

$$[\psi^+(\vec{r})\, \psi(\vec{r}),\ \psi(\vec{r}_2)\, \psi(\vec{r}_1)]$$

$$= -\psi(\vec{r})\, \psi(\vec{r}_1)\, \delta(\vec{r}-\vec{r}_2) - \psi(\vec{r}_2)\, \psi(\vec{r})\, \delta(\vec{r}-\vec{r}_1).$$

Substituting these quantities back in the original expression gives the result

$$[N, H_{int}] = \tfrac{1}{2}\int d^3x_1\, d^3x_2\, d^3x\ \ v(\vec{r}_2, \vec{r}_1)\cdot$$

$$\cdot\Big\{\big[\psi^+(\vec{r})\psi^+(\vec{r}_2)\, \delta(\vec{r}-\vec{r}_1) + \psi^+(\vec{r}_1)\psi^+(\vec{r})\delta(\vec{r}-\vec{r}_2)\big]\ \psi(\vec{r}_2)\, \psi(\vec{r}_1)$$

$$-\psi^+(\vec{r}_1)\, \psi^+(\vec{r}_2)\, \big[\psi(\vec{r})\, \psi(\vec{r}_1)\, \delta(\vec{r}-\vec{r}_2) + \psi(\vec{r}_2)\, \psi(\vec{r})\ \delta(\vec{r}-\vec{r}_1)\big]\Big\}$$

$$= \int d^3x_1\, d^3x_2\ \ v(\vec{r}_2, \vec{r}_1)\Big\{\psi^+(\vec{r}_1)\, \psi^+(\vec{r}_2)\, \psi(\vec{r}_2)\, \psi(\vec{r}_1)$$

$$- \psi^+(\vec{r}_1)\, \psi^+(\vec{r}_2)\, \psi(\vec{r}_2)\, \psi(\vec{r}_1)\Big\} = 0.$$

Note that the result is completely independent of the form of $v(\vec{r}_1, \vec{r}_2)$; N commutes not only with H_{int} but also with the operator integrand at each point of space (if N and H_{int} are both evaluated at the same time t). And in general one can show that the operator N commutes with the Hamiltonian - i. e., is a "constant of the motion" - no matter <u>what</u> the form of H_{int}, provided only that H_{int} is formed from a product of <u>n</u> ψ's and <u>n</u> ψ^+'s. (Note that this condition is not required for the <u>Hermiticity</u> of H_{int}). Thus for an interacting-particle theory of the type we have described up to now, a system which is described by a state vector $|x\rangle$ and for which at some time t_0

$$N(t_0)\,|x\rangle = n|x\rangle$$

will also satisfy the equation

$$N(t)\,|x\rangle = n|x\rangle$$

at any other time, since we have seen that

$$i\hbar\,\frac{dN(t)}{dt} = [N(t), H] = 0.$$

For systems of this type, then, the second-quantized theory offers nothing new; it simply represents a more convenient and elegant means of expressing the content of ordinary quantum theory.

From the above discussion it is now easy to see how to destroy this equivalence between the "first-quantized" and "second-quantized" theories, however. If we simply introduce an interaction term in our second-quantized Hamiltonian which does <u>not</u> conserve the number of particles, then the resulting theory will have no "first-quantized" counterpart at all - except in a very strained sense in which we introduce wave "functions" consisting of infinite row - and column - vectors of wave functions describing increasingly greater numbers of particles:

$$\begin{pmatrix} \phi^{(0)} \\ \phi^{(1)}(\vec{r}, t) \\ \phi^{(2)}(\vec{r}_1, \vec{r}_2, t) \\ \phi^{(3)}(\vec{r}_1, \vec{r}_2, \vec{r}_3, t) \\ \vdots \end{pmatrix}$$

(Such a representation of states of the system is one form of the so-called Fock-space representation of many-particle systems.) As an example of a situation where it is not only possible but also convenient to introduce a Hamiltonian which does not conserve the number of particles present, let us consider a model which is often used to represent the interaction of nucleons and mesons in the nonrelativistic limit (to the extent that such a limit can be said to exist!). We take a fermion field $\psi(\vec{r},t)$ to represent the nucleons, of course, and for the mesons we use a boson field operator $\phi(\vec{r},t)$. It is customary to ignore electromagnetic interactions, and to assume that nucleons do not interact directly with one another, but only with mesons. The nucleon-nucleon interaction will then not be a simple affair describable by a direct-interaction potential, but a rather complicated interaction which can only exist if the meson field is included in the considerations. In the absence of the meson field the nucleon Hamiltonian would just be the nucleon kinetic energy operator

$$H_{o_n} = \int d^3x \; \psi^+(\vec{r},t) \left(-\frac{\hbar^2}{2M} \nabla^2\right) \psi(\vec{r},t),$$

where M is the nucleon mass. Similarly, in the absence of the nucleon field the meson Hamiltonian is assumed to be

$$H_{o_m} = \int d^3x \; \phi^+(\vec{r},t) \left(-\frac{\hbar^2}{2\mu} \nabla^2\right) \phi(\vec{r},t),$$

where μ is the meson mass. The total Hamiltonian for the interacting system of nucleons and mesons will be the sum of these two "free" Hamiltonians and an interaction Hamiltonian which involves both fields. The simplest interaction Hamiltonian which contains both fields and conserves the number of nucleons is

$$H_{int} = \int d^3x \, d^3x' \; \psi^+(\vec{r},t)\psi(\vec{r},t)v(\vec{r},\vec{r}') \left[\phi(r',t) + \phi^+(r',t)\right] .$$

Here $v(\vec{r},\vec{r}')$ is a (real) function which must be chosen so that the interaction between nucleons and mesons predicted by this approximate theory recreates the observed results of the more complicated actual physical system as accurately as possible. The sum of these three parts,

$$H = H_{o_n} + H_{o_m} + H_{int} ,$$

is the Hamiltonian which determines the time development of the system, once we have added to the equal-time commutation relations which have already been stated for ϕ and ψ separately the stipulation that

$$\left[\phi(\vec{r},t),\ \psi(\vec{r}\,',t)\right] = \left[\phi(\vec{r},t),\ \psi^+(\vec{r}\,',t)\right] = 0,$$

as well as the adjoints of these two equations. It is then very easy to calculate the equations of motion:

$$i\hbar\,\frac{\partial\psi(\vec{r},t)}{\partial t} = \left[\psi(\vec{r},t),\ H\right]$$

$$= -\frac{\hbar^2}{2M}\,\nabla^2\psi + \left\{\int d^3x'\, v(\vec{r},\vec{r}\,')\left[\phi(\vec{r}\,',t) + \phi^+(\vec{r}\,',t)\right]\right\}\psi,$$

$$i\hbar\,\frac{\partial\phi(\vec{r},t)}{\partial t} = \left[\phi(\vec{r},t),\ H\right]$$

$$= -\frac{\hbar^2}{2\mu}\,\nabla^2\phi + \left\{\int d^3x'\,\psi^+(\vec{r}\,',t)\,\psi(\vec{r}\,',t)\,v(\vec{r}\,',\vec{r})\right\}\phi.$$

Thus we must find the operator solutions of a pair of coupled nonlinear integrodifferential equations. This is a task which, to date, can only be done approximately, by use of perturbation techniques which will be discussed later.

Actually, however, our concern here is not with the solution of these equations but rather with an investigation of the properties of the system they describe. In particular, we wish to observe that if in analogy with our previous treatments we introduce the "number operators"

$$N_n = \int d^3x\,\psi^+(\vec{r},t)\,\psi(\vec{r},t), \qquad N_m = \int d^3x\,\phi^+(\vec{r},t)\,\phi(\vec{r},t),$$

then N_n commutes with H but N_m does not. In fact, we see that

$$\left[N_m(t),\ H_{o_n}(t) + H_{o_m}(t)\right] = 0$$

but

$$\left[N_m(t),\ H_{int}(t)\right] =$$

$$= \left[\int d^3x\ \phi^+(\vec{r},t)\ \phi(\vec{r},t),\ \int d^3x_1\ d^3x_2\ \psi^+(\vec{r}_1,t)\ \cdot\right.$$

$$\left.\cdot\ \psi(\vec{r}_1,t)\ v(\vec{r}_1,\vec{r}_2)\ \left[\phi(\vec{r}_2,t) + \phi^+(\vec{r}_2,t)\right]\right]$$

$$= \int d^3x\ d^3x_1\ d^3x_2\ \psi^+(\vec{r}_1,t)\ \psi(\vec{r}_1,t)\ v(\vec{r}_1,\vec{r}_2)\ \cdot$$

$$\cdot \left\{\left[\phi^+(\vec{r},t),\ \phi(\vec{r}_2,t)\right]\ \phi(\vec{r},t) + \phi^+(\vec{r},t)\ \left[\phi(\vec{r},t),\ \phi^+(\vec{r}_2,t)\right]\right\}$$

$$= \int d^3x_1\, d^3x_2\ \psi^+(\vec{r}_1,t)\ \psi(\vec{r}_1,t)\ v(\vec{r}_1,\vec{r}_2)\ \left[\phi^+(\vec{r}_2,t) - \phi(\vec{r}_2,t)\right],$$

and this last quantity is non-zero. This means that

$$\frac{dN_m(t)}{dt} \neq 0,$$

so that the system cannot be thought of as containing a fixed number of mesons. An energy eigenstate must therefore in general actually be a linear combination of various states with all possible numbers of mesons present - for instance, an energy eigenstate with one nucleon present would be of the form

$$|E^{(1)}\rangle = \sum_{n=0}^{\infty} \int d^3x_1 \ldots d^3x_n d^3x\ C_n(\vec{r};\vec{r}_1,\ldots,\vec{r}_n)\,\phi^+(\vec{r}_1)\ldots\phi^+(\vec{r}_n)\psi^+(\vec{r})\,|0\rangle,$$

with the functions $C_n(\vec{r};\vec{r}_1,\ldots,\vec{r}_n)$ to be determined by the requirement that

$$H\,|E^{(1)}\rangle = E^{(1)}\,|E^{(1)}\rangle$$

for some number $E^{(1)}$. Similar expressions may be formed in an obvious manner for states containing larger (fixed) numbers of nucleons. This means that we might think of the energy eigenstates of the system as being states in which mesons are continually being created and annihilated with accompanying changes of state (but not of number) of the nucleons present. Obviously this is a situation that would be more difficult to represent in terms of ordinary wave mechanics than it is in the formulation used here.

c. Alternative Forms of the Theory

It is frequently convenient to transform the theory so that the operators are dependent on some set of parameters other than the spatial coordinates. For instance, we might decide to express $\psi(\vec{r}, t)$ in terms of its Fourier transform $a(\vec{p}, t)$:

$$\psi(\vec{r}, t) = \frac{1}{(2\pi\hbar)^{3/2}} \int d^3 p \; e^{i \frac{\vec{p}\cdot\vec{r}}{\hbar}} \; a(\vec{p}, t).$$

This transformation simplifies the form of our momentum operator. In fact, we find that

$$\vec{P} = \int d^3 x \, \psi^+(\vec{r}, t) \frac{\hbar}{i} \vec{\nabla} \psi(\vec{r}, t)$$

$$= \frac{1}{(2\pi\hbar)^3} \int d^3 x \, d^3 p_1 \, d^3 p_2 \, e^{-\frac{i}{\hbar} \vec{p}_1 \cdot \vec{r}} a^+(\vec{p}_1, t) \frac{\hbar}{i} \vec{\nabla} e^{\frac{i}{\hbar} \vec{p}_2 \cdot \vec{r}} a(\vec{p}_2, t)$$

$$= \int d^3 p_1 \, d^3 p_2 \; \vec{p}_2 \; a^+(\vec{p}_1, t) \, a(\vec{p}_2, t) \left(\int \frac{d^3 x}{(2\pi\hbar)^3} \; e^{\frac{i}{\hbar} \vec{r} \cdot (\vec{p}_2 - \vec{p}_1)} \right)$$

$$= \int d^3 p \; \vec{p} \; a^+(\vec{p}, t) \, a(\vec{p}, t).$$

We can also note that

$$\left[a(\vec{p}, t), a^+(\vec{p}', t)\right]_\pm = \frac{1}{(2\pi\hbar)^3} \int d^3 x \, d^3 x' e^{-\frac{i}{\hbar} \vec{p}\cdot\vec{r} + \frac{i}{\hbar} \vec{p}'\cdot\vec{r}'} \left[\psi(\vec{r}, t), \psi^+(\vec{r}', t)\right]_\pm$$

$$= \frac{1}{(2\pi\hbar)^3} \int d^3 x \; e^{\frac{i}{\hbar} \vec{r} \cdot (\vec{p}' - \vec{p})} = \delta(\vec{p} - \vec{p}'),$$

and similarly one sees that

$$\left[a(\vec{p},t),\ a(\vec{p}\,',t)\right]_{\pm} = \left[a^{+}(\vec{p},t),\ a^{+}(\vec{p}\,',t)\right]_{\pm} = 0.$$

These commutation relations and the expression

$$\vec{P} = \int d^3p\ \vec{p}\ a^{+}(\vec{p},t)\,a(\vec{p},t)$$

allow us to give an immediate interpretation to the operators $a(\vec{p},t)$ and $a^{+}(\vec{p},t)$. We observe that

$$\left[a(\vec{p},t),\ \vec{P}\right] = \int d^3p'\ \vec{p}\,'\left[a(\vec{p},t),\ a^{+}(\vec{p}\,',t)\,a(\vec{p}\,',t)\right]$$

$$= \int d^3p'\ \vec{p}\,'\ \delta(\vec{p}-\vec{p}\,')\,a(\vec{p}\,',t) = \vec{p}\ a(\vec{p},t),$$

and

$$\left[\vec{P},\ a^{+}(\vec{p},t)\right] = \vec{p}\ a^{+}(\vec{p},t).$$

Therefore by applying $\vec{P}$ to the state $a^{+}(\vec{p},t)\,|0\rangle$ we find

$$\vec{P}\,a^{+}(\vec{p},t)\,|0\rangle = \left\{\left[\vec{P},\ a^{+}(\vec{p},t)\right] + a^{+}(\vec{p},t)\,\vec{P}\right\}|0\rangle$$

$$= \vec{p}\,a^{+}(\vec{p},t)\,|0\rangle.$$

Similarly one may show that

$$\vec{P}\,a^{+}(\vec{p}_1,t)\,a^{+}(\vec{p}_2,t)\,|0\rangle = (\vec{p}_1+\vec{p}_2)\,a^{+}(\vec{p}_1,t)\,a^{+}(\vec{p}_2,t)\,|0\rangle,$$

and so on. Thus $a^{+}(\vec{p},t)$ is to be interpreted as an operator which creates (at time t) a particle of momentum $\vec{p}$. In an analogous manner it is seen that $a(\vec{p},t)$ annihilates a particle of momentum $\vec{p}$. Clearly a general one-particle state can be represented in the form

$$\int d^3p\ h(\vec{p})\ a^{+}(\vec{p},t)\ |0\rangle$$

just as well as in the form $\int d^3x\ C(\vec{r})\ \psi^{+}(\vec{r},t)\ |0\rangle$ given earlier, and so on for other particle numbers.

While introduction of the Fourier transform $a(\vec{p}, t)$ of $\psi(\vec{r}, t)$ simplifies the expression for the momentum operator $\vec{P}$, it usually complicates the Hamiltonian in the case where the system is subjected to an external potential. Still other transformations are possible, which may be of greater value in a given problem than Fourier transformation. In fact, if $u_n(\vec{r})$ is any complete orthonormal set of functions then we may expand our operator field in terms of these functions as follows:

$$\psi(\vec{r}, t) = \sum_n u_n(\vec{r})\, a_n(t).$$

The $a_n(t)$ are then a set of time-dependent operators, and we have explicitly

$$a_n(t) = \int d^3x\, u_n^*(\vec{r})\, \psi(\vec{r}, t),$$

$$a_n^+(t) = \int d^3x\, u_n(\vec{r})\, \psi^+(\vec{r}, t).$$

One then sees that

$$\left[a_n(t), a_m^+(t)\right]_\pm = \int d^3x\, d^3x'\, u_n^*(\vec{r})\, u_m(\vec{r}')\left[\psi(\vec{r}, t), \psi^+(\vec{r}', t)\right]_\pm$$

$$= \int d^3x\, u_n^*(\vec{r})\, u_m(\vec{r}) = \delta_{nm},$$

$$\left[a_n(t), a_m(t)\right]_\pm = \left[a_n^+(t), a_m^+(t)\right]_\pm = 0.$$

As an example of a situation in which a transformation of the sort described here would be useful, consider first the case where we have a system of non-interacting particles in an external potential:

$$H = \int d^3x\, \psi^+(\vec{r}, t)\left[-\frac{\hbar^2}{2m}\nabla^2 + V(\vec{r})\right]\psi(\vec{r}, t).$$

In this case we would take as our orthonormal set the solutions of the one-particle problem

$$\left[-\frac{\hbar^2}{2m}\nabla^2 + V(\vec{r})\right]u_n(\vec{r}) = E_n\, u_n(\vec{r}).$$

If we expand ψ and ψ^+ in terms of these functions, then we obtain the following form for the Hamiltonian:

$$H = \sum_{n,n'} \left\{ \int d^3x\, u^*_{n'}(\vec{r}) \left[-\frac{\hbar^2}{2m} \nabla^2 + V(\vec{r}) \right] u_n(\vec{r}) \right\} a^+_{n'}(t)\, a_n(t)$$

$$= \sum_{n,n'} E_n\, \delta_{nn'}\, a^+_{n'}(t)\, a_n(t) = \sum_n E_n\, a^+_n(t)\, a_n(t).$$

This expression can be given a very illuminating interpretation. First one may observe that

$$[a_n(t), H] = \sum_m E_m \left[a_n(t), a^+_m(t)\, a_m(t)\right]$$

$$= \sum_m E_m \left[a_n(t), a^+_m(t)\right]_\pm a_m(t) = \sum_m E_m\, \delta_{nm}\, a_m(t)$$

$$= E_n\, a_n(t),$$

and so also

$$\left[H, a^+_n(t)\right] = E_n\, a^+_n(t).$$

Therefore the one-particle state $a^+_n(t)\, |0\rangle$ satisfies the equation

$$H a^+_n(t)\, |0\rangle = \left\{ \left[H, a^+_n(t)\right] + a^+_n(t)\, H \right\} |0\rangle = E_n\, a^+_n(t)\, |0\rangle.$$

That is, we can say that $a^+_n(t)$ creates a particle with energy E_n (and thus, for a single-particle state, a particle whose wave function would be u_n). Also, it follows very easily from the commutation relations that $a^+_n(t) \cdot a_n(t)$ is a number operator for the particles with energy E_n. In fact, we see that

$$\left[a^+_n(t)\, a_n(t), a^+_m(t)\right] = a^+_n(t) \left[a_n(t), a^+_m(t)\right]_\pm$$

$$= \delta_{mn}\, a^+_n(t).$$

If $a^+_{n_1}(t)\, a^+_{n_2}(t) \ldots a^+_{n_m}(t)\, |0\rangle$ is a state containing m particles, then by adding and subtracting terms we can easily see that

$$a^+_n(t)\, a_n(t) \left[a^+_{n_1}(t)\, a^+_{n_2}(t) \ldots a^+_{n_m}(t)\, |0\rangle\right]$$

$$= \Big\{ \left[a^+_n(t)\, a_n(t),\; a^+_{n_1}(t)\right] a^+_{n_2}(t) \ldots a^+_{n_m}(t)$$

$$+ a^+_{n_1}(t) \left[a^+_n(t)\, a_n(t),\; a^+_{n_2}(t)\right] \ldots a^+_{n_m}(t)$$

$$+ \ldots + a^+_{n_1}(t)\, a^+_{n_2}(t) \ldots \left[a^+_n(t)\, a_n(t),\; a^+_{n_m}(t)\right] \Big\}\, |0\rangle.$$

Now the commutation relations just computed show that each of the commutators above is equal to $a^+_{n_j}(t)$ or to zero according to whether $n_j = n$ or $n_j \neq n$. We thus get our original state back times the number of times the operator $a^+_n(t)$ appears in the product $a^+_{n_1}(t) \ldots a^+_{n_m}(t)$. This shows that $a^+_n(t)\, a_n(t)$ is a number operator for the particles with energy E_n, as stated. The significance of the form

$$H = \sum_n E_n\, a^+_n(t)\, a_n(t)$$

for the Hamiltonian should now be obvious. If H is applied to an energy eigenstate then $a^+_n(t)\, a_n(t)$ "counts" the number of particles present which have energy E_n, and this number times the energy E_n itself which appears as a factor in the n-th term in the Hamiltonian gives the total contribution to the energy of particles of this kind. Summing over all n therefore gives the total energy for the system of particles. Note that since

$$i\hbar \frac{da_n(t)}{dt} = [a_n(t),\, H] = E_n\, a_n(t)$$

in this case, we have

$$a_n(t) = a_n(0)\, e^{-\frac{i}{\hbar} E_n t} \equiv a_n e^{-\frac{i}{\hbar} E_n t}.$$

$$+\int d^3x\ \phi^+(\vec{r},t)\left[-\frac{\hbar^2}{2M}\nabla^2+W(\vec{r})\right]\phi(\vec{r},t)$$

$$+\int d^3x\,d^3x'\ \psi^+(\vec{r},t)\,\psi(\vec{r},t)\,v(\vec{r},\vec{r}')\left[\phi^+(\vec{r}',t)+\phi(\vec{r}',t)\right].$$

In this case it is in general impossible to find an orthonormal set of functions u_n which will diagonalize the Hamiltonian in the operators a_n (i. e., insure that only products of the form $a_n^+(t)\,a_n(t)$ appear, never terms of the form $a_n^+(t)\,a_m(t)$ for $n \neq m$). A similar statement applies to the operator field ϕ. The most useful thing to do appears to be to choose two complete orthonormal sets of functions u_n and v_n satisfying the two one-particle equations

$$\left[-\frac{\hbar^2}{2m}\nabla^2+V(\vec{r})\right]u_n(\vec{r})=E_n\,u_n(\vec{r}),$$

$$\left[-\frac{\hbar^2}{2M}\nabla^2+W(\vec{r})\right]v_n(\vec{r})=w_n\,v_n(\vec{r}),$$

and to carry out the expansions

$$\psi(\vec{r},t)=\sum_n u_n(\vec{r})\,a_n(t),$$

$$\phi(\vec{r},t)=\sum_n v_n(\vec{r})\,b_n(t).$$

If we do this then the first two terms in the Hamiltonian take the form

$$\sum_n E_n\,a_n^+(t)\,a_n(t)+\sum_n w_n\,b_n^+(t)\,b_n(t),$$

while the interaction Hamiltonian becomes

$$\sum_{n,n'}\sum_m\int d^3x\,d^3x'\ u_n^*(\vec{r})\,u_{n'}(\vec{r})\,v(\vec{r},\vec{r}')\,a_n^+(t)\,a_{n'}(t)\cdot$$
$$\cdot\left[v_m^*(\vec{r}')\,b_m^+(t)+v_m(\vec{r}')\,b_m(t)\right]$$

$$=\sum_{n,n'}\sum_m C_{nn'm}\,a_n^+(t)\,a_{n'}(t)\left[b_m^+(t)+b_m(t)\right],$$

Therefore

$$a_n^+(t)\, a_n(t) \;=\; a_n^+ \, a_n$$

is really time-independent, and the number of particles with a given energy remains constant.

It is also interesting to observe that the "Pauli exclusion principle" appears in its most obvious form in the expression of the theory being discussed here. For when the field ψ is a fermion field we have seen that we have the anticommutation relations

$$\left[a_n(t),\, a_n^+(t)\right]_+ = \delta_{nm}, \quad \left[a_n(t),\, a_m(t)\right]_+ = \left[a_n^+(t),\, a_m^+(t)\right]_+ = 0,$$

and the last of these relations shows that

$$a_n^+(t)\, a_n^+(t) + a_n^+(t)\, a_n^+(t) = 0, \quad a_n^+(t)\, a_n^+(t) = 0.$$

Thus we cannot form a state

$$a_{n_1}^+(t)\, a_{n_2}^+(t) \ldots a_{n_m}^+(t)\; |0\rangle$$

in which two of the n_j are equal. Such a state would be identically zero (as is seen by anticommuting one of the identical a^+'s with intervening operators until it stands next to the other a^+ of the same kind). In the usual terminology we express this by saying that two identical fermions cannot occupy the same state at the same time. Note again that this result is built into the theory from the beginning by our choice of the equal-time anticommutation relations.

Let us consider one more example where a transformation of the form

$$\psi(\vec{r}, t) = \sum_n u_n(\vec{r})\, a_n(t)$$

might be useful, this time for the more complicated (and more realistic) case where our system consists of two types of interacting particles with a Hamiltonian

$$H = \int d^3x\, \psi^+(\vec{r}, t) \left[-\frac{\hbar^2}{2m} \nabla^2 + V(\vec{r}) \right] \psi(\vec{r}, t)$$

where $C_{nn'm} = \int u_n(\vec{r})\, u_{n'}(\vec{r})\, v(\vec{r}, \vec{r}')\, v_m(\vec{r}')\, d^3x d^3x'$ and we have taken the u's and v's all to be real (as we clearly can if we wish). Therefore an equivalent expression for our Hamiltonian is

$$H = \sum_n E_n a_n^+(t)\, a_n(t) + \sum_n w_n b_n^+(t)\, b_n(t)$$

$$+ \sum_{n,n'} \sum_m C_{nn'm}\, a_n^+(t)\, a_{n'}(t) \left[b_m^+(t) + b_m(t) \right].$$

This method of transforming the Hamiltonian for a system of interacting fields is rather frequently used in applications. The E_n which appear in H are now the energy levels for one-particle states of the ψ field in the absence of interaction with the ϕ field; and an analogous statement applies to the w_n. However, $a_n^+(t)\,|0\rangle$ is now obviously not an energy eigenstate for the complete Hamiltonian. Furthermore, the operator $a_n^+(t)\, a_n(t)$ no longer commutes with the Hamiltonian and so is not a constant of the motion. This difference between the significance of the a_n above and their significance when the total Hamiltonian is

$$H = \sum_n E_n a_n^+(t)\, a_n(t)$$

must be kept clearly in mind.

Section II. THE INTERACTION PICTURE

by

B. M. Morris

1. Introduction

It is possible to formulate quantum mechanics in several equivalent forms or "pictures." Two of these, the Schrödinger and the Heisenberg pictures, have been discussed in previous lectures and will be reviewed here. A third, the interaction or Dirac picture, is particularly useful in the case where the Hamiltonian operator can be split up into some exactly solvable unperturbed part H_0 and a perturbation V. This perturbation will be taken to be time-dependent, or to represent an interaction between different parts of the complete system or between the system and an external field, thus accounting for the name "interaction picture."

Before introducing the interaction picture, it might be helpful to review the nature of the Schrödinger and Heisenberg pictures and to state the requirements that any other picture be equivalent to the Schrödinger picture.

In the Schrödinger picture, the state vectors obey the Schrödinger equation

$$i\hbar \frac{\partial\psi_s(t)}{\partial t} = H\,\psi_s(t);$$

and if H (the Hamiltonian operator) is independent of time, they are given by

$$\psi_s(t) = e^{-\frac{i}{\hbar}Ht}\,\psi_s(0).$$

In this picture, all operators are taken to be independent of time.

In the Heisenberg picture, state vectors are independent of time while operators are not. A Heisenberg state vector is obtained from the corresponding Schrödinger state vector by the transformation

$$\psi_H = e^{\frac{i}{\hbar}Ht}\,\psi_s(t),$$

if we define the Heisenberg state vector as the Schrödinger state vector evaluated at t = 0. We can then write the expectation value of an operator in the Heisenberg picture as $\langle\psi_H^a|O_H(t)|\psi_H^b\rangle = \langle\psi_s^a(0)|O_H(t)|\psi_s^b(0)\rangle$. The corresponding expectation value in the Schrödinger picture must have this same value, so we can find the form of the operators $O_H(t)$ in terms of the O_S as follows:

$$\langle\psi_s^a(t)|O_s|\psi_s^b(t)\rangle = \langle\psi_H^a|O_H(t)|\psi_H^b\rangle,$$

$$|\psi_s^b(t)\rangle = e^{-\frac{i}{\hbar}Ht}|\psi_s^b(0)\rangle,$$

$$\langle\psi_s^a(t)| = (e^{-\frac{i}{\hbar}Ht}|\psi_s^a(0)\rangle)^+ = \langle\psi_s^a(0)|e^{\frac{i}{\hbar}Ht};$$

therefore

$$\langle\psi_s^a(0)|e^{\frac{i}{\hbar}Ht}O_s e^{-\frac{i}{\hbar}Ht}|\psi_s^b(0)\rangle$$

$$= \langle\psi_H^a|e^{\frac{i}{\hbar}Ht}O_s e^{-\frac{i}{\hbar}Ht}|\psi_H^b\rangle = \langle\psi_H^a|O_H(t)|\psi_H^b\rangle.$$

Thus

$$O_H(t) = e^{\frac{i}{\hbar}Ht}O_s e^{-\frac{i}{\hbar}Ht}.$$

The time derivative of O_H can be taken from this and is often given as the equation of motion for Heisenberg operators:

$$i\hbar\frac{dO_H}{dt} = O_H H - HO_H = [O_H, H]$$

$$\left(\frac{\partial O_s}{\partial t} = 0\right).$$

2. Transformation to Other Equivalent Representations; the Interaction Picture

As mentioned earlier, the discussion of the preceding section was only a review. One point should be noted, however, and that is the requirement that $\langle\psi_H^a|O_H|\psi_H^b\rangle = \langle\psi_s^a|O_s|\psi_s^b\rangle$. The expectation values of operators which represent physical measurements on a system must be the same in any picture. If we accept the Schrödinger picture as a valid formulation of quantum mechanics and let $|a\rangle$ represent a state of a physical system in the Schrödinger picture, then some new picture with state vector $|\bar{a}\rangle$ can also be shown to be valid if

$$|\bar{a}\rangle = U|a\rangle ,$$

where $U U^{+} = U^{+}U = 1$ - that is, if $|\bar{a}\rangle$ is obtained by a unitary transformation on $|a\rangle$. This can be demonstrated by first noting that measurement of some observable A means finding one of its eigenvalues A', the probability of the particular result being given by $|\langle A'|a\rangle|^2$. Here $|a\rangle$ denotes the state of the system and $|A'\rangle$ is an eigenvector of A: $A|A'\rangle = A'|A'\rangle$. This means that if we want to prove that $|\bar{a}\rangle$ is a valid representation we must show that:

a) each operator $\bar{A}$ corresponding to an operator A must have the same eigenvalue spectrum in $|\bar{a}\rangle$ as A has in $|a\rangle$:

b) the scalar products of $|\bar{a}\rangle$ with the transformed eigenvector $|\bar{A}'\rangle$ of the operator $\bar{A}$ must have the same value as the scalar products of $|a\rangle$ with $|A'\rangle$.

The proof that (a) and (b) hold for unitary transformations is as follows:

a) $|\bar{a}\rangle = U|a\rangle$, where $U U^{+} = 1$, or $U^{+} = U^{-1}$;

$A|A'\rangle = A'|A'\rangle$; $\bar{A} = U A U^{-1}$

(This is a generalization of the equation for transforming Schrödinger to Heisenberg operators);

$$A|A'\rangle = A'|A'\rangle \rightarrow (U^{+}\bar{A}U)U^{+}|\bar{A}'\rangle$$

$$= U^{+}\bar{A}|\bar{A}'\rangle = A'U^{+}|\bar{A}'\rangle ;$$

thus, $$U^{+}(\bar{A}|\bar{A}'\rangle - A'|\bar{A}'\rangle) = 0$$

or $\bar{A}|\bar{A}'\rangle = A'|\bar{A}'\rangle$, which says that the eigenvalues of $\bar{A}$ are the same as those of A.

b) $\langle\bar{A}'| = \langle A'|U^{+}$; $|\bar{a}\rangle = U|a\rangle$;

$$\langle\bar{A}'|\bar{a}\rangle = \langle A'|U^{+}U|a\rangle = \langle A'|a\rangle ;$$

therefore,

$$|\langle \bar{A}' | \bar{a} \rangle|^2 = |\langle A' | a \rangle|^2 .$$

Thus, the scalar products of eigenvectors with state vectors are the same in the two pictures. Having given this proof, it will be possible to show any new picture to be valid if it can be obtained from the Schrödinger picture by a unitary transformation.

With this in mind, we can now proceed to the formulation of the interaction picture. The state vectors in this new picture are given by the equation

$$\psi_I(t) = e^{\frac{i}{\hbar} H_o t} \psi_s(t),$$

where $\psi_s(t)$ obeys the Schrödinger equation

$$i\hbar \frac{\partial \psi_s(t)}{\partial t} = (H_o + V)\, \psi_s(t).$$

(H_o and V are in the Schrödinger representation.)

Since

$$\psi_I(t) = e^{\frac{i}{\hbar} H_o t} \psi_s = U\psi_s,$$

where

$$U = e^{\frac{i}{\hbar} H_o t}, \quad U^+ = e^{-\frac{i}{\hbar} H_o t},$$

and

$$UU^+ = U^+ U = 1,$$

we see that the interaction picture is a valid one.

Now by using $\psi_s = e^{-\frac{i}{\hbar} H_o t} \psi_I$ in the Schrödinger equation we can find the equation of motion for the interaction state vectors:

$$i\hbar \frac{\partial \psi_s}{\partial t} = i\hbar \frac{\partial}{\partial t} \left(e^{-\frac{i}{\hbar} H_o t} \psi_I \right) = (H_o + V)\, e^{-\frac{i}{\hbar} H_o t} \psi_I,$$

$$i\hbar \left\{ -\frac{i}{\hbar} H_o\, e^{-\frac{i}{\hbar} H_o t} \psi_I + e^{-\frac{i}{\hbar} H_o t} \frac{\partial \psi_I}{\partial t} \right\} = (H_o + V)\, e^{-\frac{i}{\hbar} H_o t} \psi_I,$$

$$i\hbar\, e^{-\frac{i}{\hbar}H_o t}\frac{\partial\psi_I}{\partial t} = V\, e^{-\frac{i}{\hbar}H_o t}\psi_I,$$

$$i\hbar\frac{\partial\psi_I}{\partial t} = e^{\frac{i}{\hbar}H_o t}\, V\, e^{-\frac{i}{\hbar}H_o t}\psi_I = V_I\,\psi_I\,.$$

This is the equation of motion for ψ_I, and it shows that the equation for transformation of operators is

$$O_I(t) = e^{\frac{i}{\hbar}H_o t}\, O_s\, e^{-\frac{i}{\hbar}H_o t}\,.$$

By differentiating this we get

$$i\hbar\frac{dO_I(t)}{dt} = O_I(t)\,H_o - H_o\,O_I(t) = [O_I(t),\ H_o],$$

the equation of motion for interaction picture operators.

We now have derived equations of motion for interaction picture state vectors and operators:

$$\left.\begin{aligned} i\hbar\frac{\partial\psi_I}{\partial t} &= V_I\,\psi_I\,, \\ i\hbar\frac{dO_I}{dt} &= [O_I,\ H_o]. \end{aligned}\right\}\quad \text{Interaction picture}$$

These can be compared with the corresponding equations for the Schrödinger and Heisenberg pictures;

$$\left.\begin{aligned} i\hbar\frac{\partial\psi_s}{\partial t} &= H\,\psi_s, \\ i\hbar\frac{dO_s}{dt} &= 0\,; \end{aligned}\right\}\quad \text{Schrödinger picture}$$

$$\left.\begin{aligned} i\hbar\frac{\partial\psi_H}{\partial t} &= 0, \\ i\hbar\frac{\partial O_H}{\partial t} &= [O_H,\ H]. \end{aligned}\right\}\quad \text{Heisenberg picture}$$

In the interaction picture both operators and state vectors "move," but their motions are governed by different parts of the total Hamiltonian. For that reason this picture is sometimes called the "intermediate" picture.

It is interesting to note that under the transformation to the interaction picture, H_o goes into itself. This can be seen if we recall the identity

$$e^{A}Be^{-A} = B + [A, B] + \frac{1}{2!}[A, [A, B]] + \frac{1}{3!}[A, [A, [A, B]]] + \ldots$$

(proved in Merzbacher, Ch. 8) and use this with the equation

$$H_{o_I} = e^{\frac{i}{\hbar}H_o t} H_o e^{-\frac{i}{\hbar}H_o t} .$$

Since $A \rightarrow iH_o t/\hbar$ and $B \rightarrow H_o$, each term in the expansion except the first involves the quantity $[H_o, H_o]$; and $[H_o, H_o] = H_oH_o - H_oH_o = 0$. Therefore the result is $(H_o)_I = (H_o)_S$, which is analogous to the previously proved fact that $(H)_H = (H)_S$.

Because of the simple form of the equation of motion for ψ_I, the interaction picture is often used in the time-dependent perturbation theory as approached from the standpoint of time-dependent unitary transformations. It is assumed that if the state of the system is known at time t_o, then the state at some later time t can be found. We also assume that if two states, $|a, t_o\rangle$ and $|b, t_o\rangle$ separately evolve into $|a, t\rangle$ and $|b, t\rangle$, then a mixture $c_1|a, t_o\rangle + c_2|b, t_o\rangle$ evolves into the mixture $c_1|a, t\rangle + c_2|b, t\rangle$. These assumptions or postulates indicate that $|a, t\rangle$ can be obtained from $|a, t_o\rangle$ by the application of some linear operator, $T(t, t_o)$. That is,

$$|a, t\rangle = T(t, t_o)\,|a, t_o\rangle .$$

In this notation there is no indication that the interaction picture is used. The above equation could apply to any picture; and the properties of $T(t, t_o)$ can be demonstrated without reference to the picture used, with one exception. The exception has to do with the unitarity of $T(t, t_o)$, and will be discussed after the other properties have been listed. These properties are the following:

(a) $T(t, t_o)\,(c_1|a, t_o\rangle + c_2|b, t_o\rangle) = c_1|a, t\rangle + c_2|b, t\rangle$

(this states the linearity of T);

(b) $T(t_2, t_0) = T(t_2, t_1)\, T(t_1, t_0)$

(this is called the group property, and it means that $T(t, t_0)$ is independent of the particular initial state $|a, t_0\rangle$) ;

(c) $[T(t, t_0)]^{-1} = T(t_0, t)$;

(d) $T(t, t) = 1$.

Although the fact that the transformation $T(t, t_0)$ is unitary does not play an important part in the later development of the time-dependent perturbation theory, it is interesting to examine this particular property in some detail. By starting with the equation

$$\psi(t) = T(t, t_0)\, \psi(t_0)$$

and substituting this $\psi(t)$ in the equation of motion

$$i \frac{\partial \psi}{\partial t} = S\, \psi \qquad\qquad (S = S^+),$$

we get the equation of motion for T:

$$i \frac{\partial T}{\partial t} = S\, T.$$

Adding the two equations

$$T^+ \left(i \frac{\partial T}{\partial t} - ST\right) = 0, \qquad \left(i \frac{\partial T^+}{\partial t} + T^+ S\right) T = 0$$

gives the relation

$$T^+ \frac{\partial T}{\partial t} + \frac{\partial T^+}{\partial t}\, T = 0\,,$$

or

$$\frac{\partial}{\partial t} (T^+ T) = 0;$$

that is, T^+T = constant. Since $T(t_0, t_0) = 1$ and $T^+(t_0, t_0) = 1$, we have the initial condition $T^+T(t_0, t_0) = 1$; so $T^+T = 1$ for all t. Thus we have shown that

$$i \frac{\partial \psi}{\partial t} = S\, \psi \text{ with } S = S^+ \implies T^+T = 1.$$

Now we can proceed in the opposite direction. We note that

$$\frac{d}{dt}(T^+T - 1) = 0$$

implies

$$T\frac{dT^+}{dt} = -\frac{dT}{dt}T^+ .$$

Then

$$T\frac{dT^+}{dt} = \left(\frac{dT}{dt}T^+\right)^+ = -\frac{dT}{dt}T^+ ,$$

so

$$\frac{dT}{dt}T^+ = -iS, \qquad \text{where } S^+ = S.$$

Then $i\frac{dT}{dt} = ST$, and consequently $i\frac{\partial\psi}{\partial t} = S\psi$. This shows that

$$T^+T = 1 \implies i\frac{\partial\psi}{\partial t} = S\psi \text{ with } S = S^+ .$$

If we now return to the notation of the interaction picture we can state that if

$$\psi_I(t) = T(t, t_o)\,\psi_I(t_o) = U(t, t_o)\,\psi_I(t_o)$$

and

$$i\hbar\frac{\partial\psi_I(t)}{\partial t} = V_I(t)\,\psi_I(t),$$

then $T \equiv U$ is a unitary transformation. This involves the assumption that V_I is Hermitian, or that it is a physically observable quantity. We will use the notation $T \rightarrow U$ from now on, since this is standard when speaking of the interaction picture. No proof will be made about the existence of $U(t, t_o)$ other than the original assumption that $\psi_I(t_o)$ does determine $\psi_I(t)$. This is essentially the principle of quantum-mechanical causality, and cannot be investigated here.

The equation of motion for U is found in the following way:

$$i\hbar\frac{\partial\psi(t)}{\partial t} = i\hbar\frac{\partial}{\partial t}\left[U(t, t_o)\,\psi(t_o)\right] = i\hbar\frac{\partial U}{\partial t}\psi(t_o)$$

$$= V_I\,U\,\psi(t_o),$$

or

$$i\hbar \frac{\partial U(t, t_o)}{\partial t} = V_I(t)\, U(t,\ t_o).$$

This can be solved by going over to an integral equation as follows:

$$\int_{t_o}^{t} i\hbar \frac{\partial U(t', t_o)}{\partial t}\, dt' = \int_{t_o}^{t} V_I(t')\, U(t', t_o)\, dt'$$

$$= i\hbar \left[U(t,\ t_o) - \underbrace{U(t_o,\ t_o)}_{1}\right],$$

$$U(t,\ t_o) = 1 - \frac{i}{\hbar} \int_{t_o}^{t} V_I\,(t')\, U(t',\ t_o)\, dt'.$$

This equation can be formally solved by the method of successive approximations:

$$U^{(o)} = 1,$$

$$U^{(1)} = 1 - \frac{i}{\hbar} \int_{t_o}^{t} V_I(t')\, U^{(o)}\, dt' = 1 - \frac{i}{\hbar} \int_{t_o}^{t} V_I(t')\, dt',$$

. . .

$$U^{(n)} = 1 - \frac{i}{\hbar} \int_{t_o}^{t} V_I(t')\, U^{(n-1)}(t',\ t_o)\, dt',$$

. . .

When we make the substitutions for $U^{(n-1)}$, $U^{(n-2)}$, etc., we get the expression

$$U(t,\ t_o) = 1 + \left(-\frac{i}{\hbar}\right) \int_{t_o}^{t} dt_1\, V_I(t_1) + \left(-\frac{i}{\hbar}\right)^2 \int_{t_o}^{t} dt_1 \int_{t_o}^{t_1} dt_2\, V_I(t_1)\, V_I(t_2)$$

$$+ \ldots + \left(-\frac{i}{\hbar}\right)^n \int_{t_o}^{t} dt_1 \int_{t_o}^{t_1} dt_2 \ldots \int_{t_o}^{t_{n-1}} dt_n \, V_I(t_1)\, V_I(t_2) \ldots V_I(t_n)$$

$$+ \ldots \quad .$$

The general term in this expansion can be written as an integral over the time interval $t_o \rightarrow t$ by introducing $\theta(t)$. That is

$$I_n = \left(-\frac{i}{\hbar}\right)^n \int_{t_o}^{t} dt_1 \int_{t_o}^{t} dt_2 \ldots \int_{t_o}^{t} dt_n \, \theta(t_1 - t_2)\, \theta(t_2 - t_3) \ldots \theta(t_{n-1} - t_n) \cdot$$

$$\cdot V_I(t_1)\, V_I(t_2) \ldots V_I(t_n) \, ,$$

where

$$\theta(t) = \begin{cases} 1, & t > 0 \\ 0, & t < 0 \end{cases} .$$

If it is possible to change the order of integration then

$$\int_{t_o}^{t} dt_1 \ldots \int_{t_o}^{t} dt_n \, f(t_1, \ldots, t_n) = \frac{1}{n!} \sum_p \int_{t_o}^{t} dt_1 \ldots \int_{t_o}^{t} dt_n \, f(t_1, \ldots t_n),$$

where $\sum_p$ indicates a sum over all permutations of the variables $t_1 \ldots t_n$. The introduction of $\theta(t)$ and $\sum_p$ can be considered as a single operation P which is defined as

$$P[V_I(t_1) \ldots V_I(t_n)] \equiv \sum_p \theta(t_{a_1} - t_{a_2}) \ldots \theta(t_{a_{n-1}} - t_{a_n}) \cdot$$

$$\cdot V_I(t_{a_1}) \ldots V_I(t_{a_n}) \, .$$

This allows us to write

$$U(t, t_o) = 1 + \sum_{n=1}^{\infty} I_n$$

$$= 1 + \sum_{n=1}^{\infty} \left(-\frac{i}{\hbar}\right)^n \frac{1}{n!} \int_{t_o}^{t} dt_1 \ldots \int_{t_o}^{t} dt_n \, P\left[V_I(t_1) \ldots V_I(t_n)\right].$$

The operator P is called the "Dyson chronological operator."

To make things clearer we can examine the specific case n = 2. There our definition gives

$$2 \frac{I_2}{\left(-\frac{i}{\hbar}\right)^2} = \int_{t_o}^{t} dt_1 \int_{t_o}^{t} dt_2 \quad P\left[V_I(t_1) \, V_I(t_2)\right]$$

$$= \int_{t_o}^{t} dt_1 \int_{t_o}^{t} dt_2 \sum_{p} \theta(t_{a_1} - t_{a_2}) \, V_I(t_{a_1}) \, V_I(t_{a_2})$$

$$= \int_{t_o}^{t} dt_1 \int_{t_o}^{t} dt_2 \quad \theta(t_1 - t_2) \, V_I(t_1) \, V_I(t_2)$$

$$+ \int_{t_o}^{t} dt_1 \int_{t_o}^{t} dt_2 \quad \theta(t_2 - t_1) \, V_I(t_2) \, V_I(t_1)$$

$$= \underbrace{\int_{t_o}^{t} dt_1 \int_{t_o}^{t_1} dt_2 \, V_I(t_1) \, V_I(t_2)}_{A} + \underbrace{\int_{t_o}^{t} dt_1 \int_{t_1}^{t} dt_2 \, V_I(t_2) \, V_I(t_1)}_{B}.$$

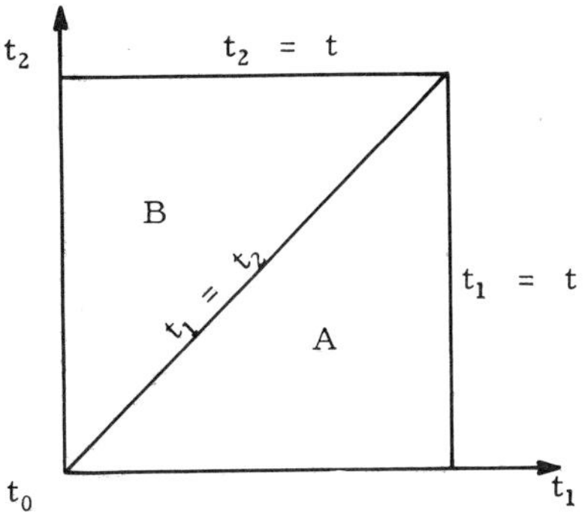

The integral as written with P unexpanded is taken over the whole square in the diagram. Sections A and B correspond to the integrals A and B.

The equality of the integrals A and B, although indicated by the diagram, can be shown analytically. We work with B, but start with the form including $\theta(t_2 - t_1)$. We see that

$$\int_{t_0}^{t} dt_1 \int_{t_0}^{t} dt_2 \;\theta(t_2 - t_1)\, V_I(t_2)\, V_I(t_1)$$

$$= \int_{t_0}^{t} dt_2 \int_{t_0}^{t} dt_1 \;\theta(t_2 - t_1)\, V_I(t_2)\, V_I(t_1)$$

$$= \int_{t_0}^{t} dt_2 \int_{t_0}^{t_2} dt_1 \; V_I(t_2)\, V_I(t_1),$$

where we have just carried out the integrals over the variables t_1 and t_2 in the reverse order. Next we interchange the dummy variables t_1 and t_2 - i. e., we let $t_1 \rightarrow t_2$ and $t_2 \rightarrow t_1$ - and get

$$B = \int_{t_0}^{t} dt_1 \int_{t_0}^{t_1} dt_2 \; V_I(t_1)\, V_I(t_2) = A.$$

Therefore

$$2 \frac{I_2}{\left(-\frac{i}{\hbar}\right)^2} = A + B = 2A = 2!A,$$

or written out in full

$$I_2 = (-\frac{i}{\hbar})^2 \int_{t_o}^{t} dt_1 \int_{t_o}^{t_1} dt_2 \; V_I(t_1)\, V_I(t_2)$$

$$= \frac{1}{2!} (-\frac{i}{\hbar})^2 \int_{t_o}^{t} dt_1 \int_{t_o}^{t} dt_2 \; P\left[V_I(t_1)\, V_I(t_2)\right];$$

this is what we started out to show.

3. Perturbation Theory in the Interaction Picture

The interaction picture is perhaps the one best suited to a formulation of perturbation theory. We will attempt to show that the results of the interaction picture and ordinary perturbation theory are in agreement. We first review the perturbation theory as treated in ordinary quantum mechanics.

(A) In the time-independent theory we have

$$(H_o + V)|m\rangle_{exact} = E_m |m\rangle_{exact},$$

where

$$H_o |m\rangle^{(o)} = E_m^o \, |m\rangle^{(o)}.$$

We seek $|m\rangle_{exact}$ and E_m. They are given to first order in V by

$$|m\rangle^{(1)} = |m\rangle^{(o)} + \sum_k{}' \frac{|k\rangle^{(o)} \; {}^{(o)}\langle k|V|m\rangle^{(o)}}{E_m^o - E_k^o},$$

$$E_m^{(1)} = E_m^o + {}^{(o)}\langle m|V|m\rangle^{(o)}.$$

(We will consider only the comparison between the first order results of the interaction picture and of ordinary quantum mechanics.)

(B) In the case of the time-dependent theory we consider a Hamiltonian of the sort

$$H = H_o + V(t).$$

Let the $\psi_n^{(o)}$ be determined by the conditions

$$H_o \psi_n^{(o)} = E_n^{(o)} \psi_n^{(o)}, \quad (\psi_n^{(o)}, \psi_k^{(o)}) = \delta_{nk};$$

then write the solution of the time-dependent Schrödinger equation in the form

$$\psi(t) = \sum_n c_n(t)\, e^{-\frac{i E_n^{(o)}}{\hbar} t}\, \psi_n^{(o)},$$

where

$$c_n(t) = (\psi_n^{(o)}, \psi(t))\, e^{\frac{i E_n^{(o)}}{\hbar} t}.$$

Since $\psi(t)$ must satisfy

$$i\hbar \frac{d\psi}{dt} = (H_o + V)\psi,$$

we see that

$$i\hbar \frac{dc_k}{dt} = \sum_n c_n V_{kn}\, e^{i\omega_{kn} t},$$

where

$$\omega_{kn} = \frac{E_k^{(o)} - E_n^{(o)}}{\hbar}, \quad V_{kn} = (\psi_k^{(o)}, V\psi_n^{(o)}).$$

Now for some fixed s we take $c_s(-\infty) = 1$ and $c_k(-\infty) = 0$, $k \neq s$, so that for $k \neq s$

$$i\hbar \frac{dc_k}{dt} = V_{ks}\, e^{i\omega_{ks} t}$$

for values of t such that $c_k(t) << c_s(t) \approx 1$ $(k \neq s)$. Integrating from $-\infty$ to t we get

$$c_k(t) = -\frac{i}{\hbar}\int_{-\infty}^{t} V_{ks}\, e^{i\omega_{ks}t'}\, dt',$$

which is the probability amplitude that the system is in the k-th state at time t. Later we shall compare these results with those obtained from the interaction-picture perturbation expansion.

We have previously shown that in the interaction picture

$$i\hbar \frac{\partial \psi_I(t)}{\partial t} = V_I(t)\, \psi_I(t),$$

where

$$\psi_I(t) = e^{\frac{i}{\hbar}H_0 t}\, \psi_s(t),$$

$$V_I(t) = e^{\frac{i}{\hbar}H_0 t}\, V(t)\, e^{-\frac{i}{\hbar}H_0 t},$$

and

$$i\hbar \frac{\partial \psi_s}{\partial t} = H\psi_s = (H_0 + V)\psi_s.$$

We also have

$$\psi_I(t) = U(t, t_0)\, \psi_I(t_0),$$

where

$$U(t, t_0) = 1 + \sum_{n=1}^{\infty} \frac{1}{n!}\left(\frac{-i}{\hbar}\right)^n \int_{t_0}^{t} dt_1 \ldots \int_{t_0}^{t} dt_n\, P[V_I(t_1)\ldots V_I(t_n)]$$

$$= P \exp\left[-\frac{i}{\hbar}\int_{t_0}^{t} V_I(t')\, dt'\right].$$

The approach we shall use is that of setting up a general perturbation theory in order to find $\psi_I(t)$ as an exact eigenstate of H in terms of $\psi_I(-\infty)$, which is taken to be an exact eigenstate of H_0. We will be interested primarily in the ground state and in the first-order corrections to state vectors and energies.

In order to set up a perturbation theory for the ground state in the interaction picture we break the total Hamiltonian up into an H_0 and a V such that the eigenstates $|\Phi_0\rangle$ of H_0 are known. We want to find the exact ground state of the total Hamiltonian H and the difference in energy ΔE between the unperturbed ground state energy and the exact energy. Thus we have

Φ or $|\Phi\rangle \rightarrow$ lowest exact eigenstate of H;

Φ_0 or $|\Phi_0\rangle \rightarrow$ lowest unperturbed eigenstate;

$E_0 \rightarrow$ lowest energy eigenvalue of H_0;

$H_0|\Phi_0\rangle = E_0|\Phi_0\rangle$;

$\Delta E \rightarrow$ shift in ground state energy.

Note that a useful expression for ΔE can be found as follows. We have

$$H|\Phi\rangle = (H_0 + V)|\Phi\rangle = (E_0 + \Delta E)|\Phi\rangle,$$

so

$$\langle\Phi_0|H|\Phi\rangle = \langle\Phi_0|H_0|\Phi\rangle + \langle\Phi_0|V|\Phi\rangle$$

$$= (E_0 + \Delta E)\langle\Phi_0|\Phi\rangle.$$

By subtracting

$$\langle\Phi_0|H_0|\Phi\rangle = E_o\langle\Phi_o|\Phi\rangle$$

from

$$\langle \Phi_o | H_o + V | \Phi \rangle = (E_o + \Delta E) \langle \Phi_o | \Phi \rangle$$

we get

$$\langle \Phi_o | V | \Phi \rangle = \Delta E \langle \Phi_o | \Phi \rangle,$$

or

$$\Delta E = \frac{\langle \Phi_o | V | \Phi \rangle}{\langle \Phi_o | \Phi \rangle} .$$

The calculation of the exact perturbed ground state wave function is necessary for use of the above expression for ΔE. To make this calculation we introduce a factor $e^{-\alpha|t|}$ in the expression for V so that

$$H = H_o + e^{-\alpha|t|} V,$$

$$V_I = e^{\frac{i}{\hbar} H_o t} V e^{-\frac{i}{\hbar} H_o t} e^{-\alpha|t|},$$

with the understanding that after all calculations have been made we will let the positive number α go to zero. As t varies from $-\infty$ to 0, H varies from H_o to $H_o + V$. Thus, we consider the perturbation to be switched on slowly. As t goes to $+\infty$, it is switched off. The reason for doing this switching on and off is that we want to include only those state vectors which have no time dependence in the infinite past. Suppose, for instance, that we calculate an eigenstate $\psi_I(t)$ in the interaction picture. Then from previous lectures we have

$$\psi_I(t) = e^{\frac{i}{\hbar} H_o t} \psi_s(t),$$

$$\psi_s(t) = e^{-\frac{i}{\hbar} H t} \psi_s(o),$$

$$\psi_I(t) = e^{\frac{i}{\hbar} H_o t} e^{-\frac{i}{\hbar} Ht} \psi_s(o);$$

and also - in view of the above discussion -

$$H = H_o + V e^{-\alpha|t|}.$$

Now we have

$$i\hbar \frac{\partial \psi_I}{\partial t} = e^{-\alpha|t|} e^{\frac{i}{\hbar} H_o t} V e^{-\frac{i}{\hbar} H_o t} \Psi_I \xrightarrow[t \to -\infty]{} 0,$$

so we see that

$$\psi_I(t) \xrightarrow[t \to -\infty]{} \text{constant.}$$

If we had used $H = H_o + V$, the state vector might have been time-dependent in the infinite past.

We are now ready to deal with the question of the state vector $|\Phi\rangle$. We will take it to be given by

$$|\Phi\rangle = \frac{U(0, -\infty)|\Phi_o\rangle}{\langle\Phi_o|U(0, -\infty)|\Phi_o\rangle}.$$

This is known as the Adiabatic Theorem because of the slow switching on of the interaction. To justify the use of the thus-defined state vector, we will show that $e^{-\frac{i}{\hbar} H_o t} U(t, -\infty)|\Phi_o\rangle$ obeys the Schrödinger equation and that we can get the same expansion coefficients or matrix elements as obtained in the ordinary perturbation theory.

1. The interaction picture state vector is $U(t, -\infty) \, | \Phi_o \rangle$, so the Schrödinger state vector is $e^{-\frac{i}{\hbar} H_o t} \, U(t, -\infty) \, | \Phi_o \rangle$ and, therefore, must satisfy the equation

$$i\hbar \frac{\partial}{\partial t} \psi_{Schröd.} = (H_o + V e^{-a|t|}) \, \psi_{Schröd.}$$

It follows from above that

$$i\hbar \frac{\partial}{\partial t} \left[e^{-\frac{i}{\hbar} H_o t} \, | \Phi \rangle \right]$$

$$= i\hbar \left[-\frac{i}{\hbar} H_o \, e^{-\frac{i}{\hbar} H_o t} \, | \Phi \rangle + e^{-\frac{i}{\hbar} H_o t} \frac{\partial}{\partial t} \, | \Phi \rangle \right]$$

$$= (H_o + V e^{-a|t|}) \, e^{-\frac{i}{\hbar} H_o t} \, | \Phi \rangle .$$

However, if $| \Phi \rangle$ is an interaction picture state vector, we already know that it satisfies this equation. That is,

$$i\hbar e^{-\frac{i}{\hbar} H_o t} \frac{\partial}{\partial t} \, | \Phi \rangle = V e^{-a|t|} \, e^{-\frac{i}{\hbar} H_o t} \, | \Phi \rangle ;$$

so, the state vector $| \Phi \rangle$ we have chosen does check out as a solution of the proper equation.

2. Now we calculate the matrix element of $U(t, -\infty)$ between an eigenstate $| k \rangle$ of H_o and the unperturbed ground state $| \Phi_o \rangle$, which will be denoted by $| O \rangle$. We want to obtain the value of

$$\langle k \, | \, U(t, -\infty) \, | \, O \rangle = \langle k \, | \, 1 + \left(-\frac{i}{\hbar} \right) \int_{-\infty}^{t} dt_1 \, V_I e^{-a|t_1|} + \ldots \, | \, O \rangle ,$$

but we will retain only the first-order terms for our purposes here. Using the orthogonality condition $\langle k \, | \, O \rangle = 0$, we get

$$\langle k \, | \, U^{(1)}(t, -\infty) \, | \, O \rangle = -\frac{i}{h} \int_{-\infty}^{t} dt_1 \langle k \, | \, V_I \, | \, O \rangle \, e^{-a|t_1|} .$$

The factor $\langle k|V_I|0\rangle$ can be changed in the following way:

$$H_o|0\rangle = E_o|0\rangle, \quad H_o|k\rangle = E_k|k\rangle,$$

and therefore

$$e^{\frac{i}{\hbar}H_o t}|k\rangle = e^{\frac{i}{\hbar}E_k t}|k\rangle, \quad e^{\frac{i}{\hbar}H_o t}|0\rangle = e^{\frac{i}{\hbar}E_o t}|0\rangle;$$

thus,

$$\langle k|V_I|0\rangle = \langle k|e^{\frac{i}{\hbar}H_o t}\, V\, e^{-\frac{i}{\hbar}H_o t}|0\rangle$$

$$= \langle k|e^{\frac{i}{\hbar}E_k t}\, V\, e^{-\frac{i}{\hbar}E_o t}|0\rangle,$$

or

$$\langle k|V_I|0\rangle = \langle k|V|0\rangle e^{\frac{i}{\hbar}(E_k-E_o)t} = V_{ko}\, e^{i\omega_{ko}t},$$

where

$$\omega_{ko} = \frac{1}{\hbar}(E_k-E_o), \quad V_{ko} = \langle k|V|0\rangle.$$

Accordingly, we obtain the desired matrix element

$$\langle k|U^{(1)}(t,-\infty)|0\rangle = -\frac{i}{\hbar}\int_{-\infty}^{t} dt_1\, \langle k|V|0\rangle e^{i(\omega_{ko}-i\alpha)t_1}$$

$$= -\frac{i}{\hbar}\int_{-\infty}^{t} dt'\, V_{ko}\, e^{i(\omega_{ko}-i\alpha)t'}$$

This is to be compared with the result of the time-dependent perturbation theory stated earlier, which was

$$c_k(t) = -\frac{i}{\hbar}\int_{-\infty}^{t} dt'\, V_{ko}\, e^{i\omega_{ko}t'}.$$

The only difference is the presence of α, but this is taken care of by eventually letting it go to zero.

Now if we let t approach zero and take V to be independent of time, we get the matrix element

$$\langle k | U^{(1)}(0,-\infty) | 0 \rangle = -\frac{i}{\hbar} \langle k | V | 0 \rangle \int_{-\infty}^{0} e^{i(\omega_{ko} - i\alpha) t'} \, dt' \quad .$$

$$= - \frac{\langle k | V | 0 \rangle}{E_k - E_o - i\alpha\hbar} \quad .$$

Rewriting the results of ordinary time-independent perturbation theory (see the discussion already given), the ground state form gives

$$| 0 \rangle^{(1)} = | 0 \rangle^{(0)} + \sum_l{}' \frac{| l \rangle \langle l | V | 0 \rangle}{E_o - E_l} ,$$

so that

$$\langle k | O \rangle^{(1)} = \overset{0}{\cancel{\langle k | 0 \rangle^{(0)}}} + \sum_l{}' \overset{\delta_{kl}}{\cancel{\langle k | l \rangle}} \frac{\langle l | V | 0 \rangle}{E_o - E_l}$$

$$= - \frac{\langle k | V | 0 \rangle}{E_k - E_o} \quad .$$

The results of the two theories agree except for the presence of α, which vanishes.

If we recall that the expression for the energy correction is

$$\Delta E = \frac{\langle \Phi_o | V | \Phi \rangle}{\langle \Phi_o | \Phi \rangle}$$

and that $|\Phi\rangle$ is given by the adiabatic theorem as

$$|\Phi\rangle = \frac{U(0,-\infty)|\Phi_o\rangle}{\langle\Phi_o|U(0,-\infty)|\Phi_o\rangle} ,$$

then we arrive at the expression

$$\Delta E = \frac{\langle\Phi_o|VU(0,-\infty)|\Phi_o\rangle}{\langle\Phi_o|U(0,-\infty)|\Phi_o\rangle} .$$

To check this result against the first-order approximation of the ordinary perturbation theory, we include only $U^{(o)}$ in the expansion for U and obtain

$$\Delta E^{(1)} = \frac{\langle\Phi_o|VU^{(o)}|\Phi_o\rangle}{\langle\Phi_o|U^{(o)}|\Phi_o\rangle} = \langle 0|V|0\rangle.$$

This does agree with the ordinary theory, so we have shown that the adiabatic theorem gives the proper first-order matrix elements and energy corrections.

Since, in general, we seek higher-order corrections to both wave functions and energies than those given above, we include an example of how higher-order matrix elements are handled. The second-order matrix element is

$$\langle k|U^{(2)}(0,-\infty)|0\rangle = \left(-\frac{i}{\hbar}\right)^2 \int_{-\infty}^{o} dt_1 \int_{-\infty}^{t_1} dt_2 \langle k|V_I(t_1)V_I(t_2)|O\rangle e^{\alpha(t_1+t_2)} .$$

We use our previous equations and a well-known transformation formula for matrix elements to write

$$\langle k|V_I(t_1)V_I(t_2)|O\rangle = \sum_p \langle k|V|p\rangle e^{\frac{i}{\hbar}(E_k-E_p)t_1} \langle p|V|0\rangle e^{\frac{i}{\hbar}(E_p-E_o)t_2} .$$

Taking V to be independent of time and performing the integration over t_2 gives

$$\langle k|U^{(2)}|0\rangle = \left(-\frac{i}{\hbar}\right)^2 \int_{-\infty}^{0} dt_1 \sum_p \langle k|V|p\rangle e^{\frac{i}{\hbar}(E_k - E_p - i\alpha\hbar)t_1} \langle p|V|0\rangle .$$

$$\cdot \left\{ \left[\frac{\hbar}{i} \frac{1}{E_p - E_o - i\alpha\hbar} e^{\frac{i}{\hbar}(E_p - E_o - i\alpha\hbar)t_2} \right] \Bigg|_{-\infty}^{t_1} \right\}$$

$$= \left(-\frac{i}{\hbar}\right)^2 \int_{-\infty}^{0} dt_1 \sum_p \frac{\langle k|V|p\rangle\langle p|V|0\rangle}{E_p - E_o - i\alpha\hbar} \left(\frac{\hbar}{i}\right) e^{\frac{i}{\hbar}(E_k - E_o - 2i\alpha\hbar)t_1} ,$$

since

$$\lim_{t_2 \to -\infty} e^{\frac{i}{\hbar}(E_p - E_o)t_2} e^{\alpha t_2} = 0.$$

Thus, we obtain the familiar result

$$\langle k|U^{(2)}|0\rangle = \frac{i}{\hbar} \sum_p \frac{\langle k|V|p\rangle\langle p|V|0\rangle}{E_p - E_o - i\alpha\hbar} \frac{e^{\frac{i}{\hbar}(E_k - E_o - 2i\alpha\hbar)t_1}}{\frac{i}{\hbar}(E_k - E_o - 2i\alpha\hbar)} \Bigg|_{-\infty}^{0}$$

$$= \sum_p \frac{\langle k|V|p\rangle\langle p|V|0\rangle}{(E_k - E_o - 2i\alpha\hbar)(E_p - E_o - i\alpha\hbar)} .$$

We have presented here only a simple justification for future use of the two basic formulas

$$|\Phi\rangle = \frac{U(0, -\infty)|\Phi_o\rangle}{\langle\Phi_o|U(0, -\infty)|\Phi_o\rangle} ,$$

$$\Delta E = \frac{\left\langle \Phi_o \middle| VU(0,-\infty) \middle| \Phi_o \right\rangle}{\left\langle \Phi_o \middle| U(0,-\infty) \middle| \Phi_o \right\rangle} .$$

Gell-Mann and Low have given a rigorous proof of the adiabatic theorem in which they show that $|\Phi\rangle$ is an eigenstate of the total Hamiltonian

$$H = H_o + Ve^{-\alpha|t|}$$

(Phys. Rev. 84, 350 (1951)). Their proof is discussed in detail in Schweber's Relativistic Quantum Field Theory.

In conclusion, we might note some of the advantages of the interaction picture formulation of quantum mechanics and perturbation theory. For one thing, the notation is extremely compact when dealing with formal solutions. Secondly, introducing the cut-off parameter α and taking the limit $\alpha \to$ zero after the calculations have been made, permits us to avoid the problems associated with the poles encountered in the ordinary perturbation theory. It has also been demonstrated that higher-order results are more easily obtained in the interaction picture. Finally, the concept of the "S-matrix" which is useful in relativistic field theory follows as a special case of the U-matrix discussed above. This operator is simply defined as

$$S \equiv U(\infty, -\infty) = P\left\{ \exp\left[-\frac{i}{h} \int_{-\infty}^{\infty} V_I(t') \, dt' \right] \right\} ;$$

it is an operator which connects states in the infinite past with states in the infinite future, and it is, therefore, a useful quantity to consider when one is dealing with scattering rather than with the ground-state problems discussed here.

Section III. PERTURBATION THEORY AND DIAGRAM TECHNIQUES

by

C. Alton Coulter

1. Introduction

Let us briefly recall the principal points of the preceding discussion given by Mr. Morris. In that development, it was assumed that we were dealing with a physical system whose dynamics were described by a Hamiltonian

$$H = H_o + H_{int},$$

where H_o is a part of H whose eigenstate problem we can (presumably) solve exactly. For each Schrödinger state vector $|\Psi_S(t)\rangle$ of the system, a corresponding "interaction picture" state vector $|\Psi_I(t)\rangle$ was introduced by the equation

$$|\Psi_I(t)\rangle = e^{\frac{i}{\hbar} H_o t} |\Psi_S(t)\rangle .$$

The vectors $|\Psi_I(t)\rangle$ were found to satisfy the equation

$$i\hbar \frac{d}{dt} |\Psi_I(t)\rangle = H_{int}(t) \, |\Psi_I(t)\rangle ,$$

where

$$H_{int}(t) = e^{\frac{i}{\hbar} H_o t} H_{int} \, e^{-\frac{i}{\hbar} H_o t} .$$

An operator $U(t, t_o)$ was introduced to connect the interaction-picture state vector at time t_o with that at time t:

$$|\Psi_I(t)\rangle = U(t, t_o) \, |\Psi_I(t_o)\rangle .$$

As a result of this definition, $U(t, t_o)$ is seen to satisfy the equation

$$i\hbar \frac{dU(t, t_o)}{dt} = H_{int}(t) \, U(t, t_o).$$

This equation and the obvious boundary condition

$$U(t, t) = 1$$

are both summarized in the integral equation

$$U(t, t_o) = 1 - \frac{i}{\hbar} \int_{t_o}^{t} dt' \, H_{int}(t') \, U(t', t_o),$$

and from the integral equation the formal solution

$$U(t, t_o) = 1 + \left(-\frac{i}{\hbar}\right) \int_{t_o}^{t} dt_1 \, H_{int}(t_1)$$

$$+ \left(-\frac{i}{\hbar}\right)^2 \int_{t_o}^{t} dt_1 \int_{t_o}^{t_1} dt_2 \, H_{int}(t_1) \, H_{int}(t_2) + \cdots$$

$$= P \left[\exp\left(-\frac{i}{\hbar} \int_{t_o}^{t} dt' \, H_{int}(t')\right)\right]$$

is easily obtained. Furthermore, it was seen that if we introduce an exponential "cut-off factor" $e^{-a|t|}$ into the definition of $H_{int}(t)$,

$$H'_a(t) = e^{-a|t|} H_{int}(t) = e^{-a|t|} e^{\frac{i}{\hbar} H_o t} H_{int} \, e^{-\frac{i}{\hbar} H_o t},$$

and define a corresponding $U_a(t, t_o)$ by the equation

$$U_a(t, t_o) = P \left[\exp\left(-\frac{i}{\hbar} \int_{t_o}^{t} dt' \, H'_a(t)\right)\right],$$

then the following statements may be made: let $|O\rangle$ be the (nondegenerate) ground state of H_o; then the exact ground state $|O)$ of $H = H_o + H_{int}$ is given by

$$|O) = \lim_{a \to 0+} \frac{U_a(0, -\infty)\,|O\rangle}{\langle O|\, U_a(0, -\infty)\,|O\rangle}; \qquad (1)$$

and

$$H\,|0) = (E_0 + \Delta E)\,|0) \quad , \tag{1}$$

where

$$H_0 \;|0\rangle = E_0 \;|0\rangle$$

and

$$\Delta E = \lim_{a\to 0+} \frac{\langle 0|\, H_{int} U_a(0,-\infty)\,|0\rangle}{\langle 0|\, U_a(0,-\infty)\,|0\rangle} \quad . \tag{2}$$

Equations (1) and (2) together with the expansion for $U(t, t_0)$ in terms of a time-ordered exponential yield a very useful perturbation theory, and it will be our purpose in the next few lectures to examine some of the basic techniques and results of this theory.

2. General Form of the Perturbation Expansion for a System of Fermions

We shall consider an application of the perturbation theory to a system of fermions which are in an externally-produced field and which also interact with one another. The manner in which the treatment can be extended to boson fields and to interacting fermion and boson fields will be obvious. We shall again consider only spinless fermions, so the Hamiltonian will have the familiar form

$$H = \int d^3x \;\psi^+(\vec{r}) \left[-\frac{\hbar^2}{2m}\nabla^2 + V(\vec{r}) \right] \psi(\vec{r})$$
$$+ \frac{1}{2}\int d^3x\, d^3x' \;\psi^+(\vec{r})\,\psi^+(\vec{r}')\; v(\vec{r},\vec{r}')\;\psi(\vec{r}')\,\psi(\vec{r}).$$

Here $V(\vec{r})$ is the external potential and $v(\vec{r},\vec{r}')$ describes the two-body fermion-fermion interaction. Since H is independent of the time, it has been assumed that the ψ's are evaluated at $t = 0$, and the time argument is not explicitly indicated.

We wish to separate H into an H_0 which can be handled exactly and an H_{int} which cannot. Clearly the term

$$\frac{1}{2}\int d^3x\, d^3x' \;\psi^+(\vec{r})\,\psi^+(\vec{r}')\; v(\vec{r},\vec{r}')\;\psi(\vec{r}')\,\psi(\vec{r})$$

goes into H_{int}! It is sometimes convenient, however, to include in H_{int} also a one-particle potential term

$$-\int d^3 x\, \psi^+(\vec{r})\, W(\vec{r})\, \psi(\vec{r})$$

which makes the perturbation series converge faster; a particularly useful choice for this purpose is the Hartree-Fock potential. We shall therefore write

$$H = H_o + H_{int},$$

$$H_o = \int d^3 x\, \psi^+(\vec{r}) \left[-\frac{h^2}{2m}\nabla^2 + V(\vec{r}) + W(\vec{r})\right] \psi(\vec{r}), \tag{3}$$

$$H_{int} = \frac{1}{2}\int d^3 x\, d^3 x'\, \psi^+(\vec{r})\, \psi^+(\vec{r}')\, v(\vec{r}, \vec{r}')\, \psi(\vec{r}')\, \psi(\vec{r}) - \int d^3 x\, \psi^+(\vec{r})\, W(\vec{r})\, \psi(\vec{r}), \tag{4}$$

so as to include all the various possibilities - including the case $W = 0$.

Usually the quantity of most immediate physical interest in the study of a given system is the ground state energy. For this reason we shall concern ourselves here solely with the calculation of the quantity ΔE, the difference between the energy E of the exact ground state and the energy E_o (which we supposedly can calculate) of the ground state of H_o. The expression for ΔE has already been given:

$$\Delta E = \lim_{a \to 0+} \frac{\langle 0|\, H_{int}\, U_a(0, -\infty)\, |0\rangle}{\langle 0|\, U_a(0, -\infty)\, |0\rangle},$$

where

$$U_a(t, t_o) = P\left[\exp\left(-\frac{i}{\hbar}\int_{t_o}^{t} H_a'(t')\, dt'\right)\right].$$

The equation of motion for $U_a(t, t_o)$ is now

$$i\hbar \frac{dU_a(t, t_o)}{dt} = H_a'(t)\, U_a(t, t_o),$$

where

$$H'_\alpha(t) = e^{-\alpha|t|} e^{\frac{i}{\hbar} H_o t} H_{int} e^{-\frac{i}{\hbar} H_o t},$$

and this fact allows us to write ΔE in the more convenient form

$$\Delta E = i\hbar \lim_{\alpha \to 0+} \left[\frac{d}{dt} \frac{\langle O | U_\alpha(t, -\infty)|O\rangle}{\langle O | U_\alpha(0, -\infty)|O\rangle} \right]_{t=0}. \tag{5}$$

Our job will then be to evaluate the time-dependent quantity

$$\frac{\langle O | U_\alpha(t, -\infty) | O\rangle}{\langle O | U_\alpha(0, -\infty) |O\rangle}.$$

We shall do this by utilizing the series expansion for $U_\alpha(t, t_o)$.

We begin by examining the nature of $|O\rangle$ and of $H'_\alpha(t)$ more closely. $|O\rangle$ is, by definition, the ground state of the Hamiltonian

$$H_o = \int d^3 x\, \psi^+(\vec{r}) \left[-\frac{\hbar^2}{2m} \nabla^2 + V(\vec{r}) + W(\vec{r}) \right] \psi(\vec{r}).$$

If the functions ϕ_n are the one-particle wave functions for this Hamiltonian,

$$\left[-\frac{\hbar^2}{2m} \nabla^2 + V(\vec{r}) + W(\vec{r}) \right] \phi_n(\vec{r}) = E_n\, \phi_n(\vec{r})$$

$$(E_1 \leq E_2 \leq \ldots),$$

and if we write

$$\psi(\vec{r}) = \sum_n \phi_n(\vec{r})\, a_n,$$

then the ground state of H_o for the system is

$$|O\rangle = a_1^+ a_2^+ \ldots a_N^+ |\text{vacuum state}\rangle. \tag{6}$$

(Note that the notation $|0\rangle$ which was formerly used for the vacuum state is now being used for the N-fermion ground state of the system. The formal analogies which prompt this will become clear later.) The explicit form for $|0\rangle$ which is given in Equation (6) will soon be of importance. As for $H'_\alpha(t)$, it is by definition the operator

$$H'_\alpha(t) = e^{-\alpha|t|}\left\{\frac{1}{2}\int d^3 x\, d^3 x'\, \psi^+(\vec{r},t)\, \psi^+(\vec{r'},t)\, v(\vec{r},\vec{r'})\, \psi(\vec{r'},t)\, \psi(\vec{r},t)\right.$$

$$\left. - \int d^3 x\, \psi^+(\vec{r},t)\, W(\vec{r})\, \psi(\vec{r},t)\right\},$$

where

$$\psi(\vec{r},t) = e^{\frac{i}{\hbar}H_o t}\, \psi(\vec{r})\, e^{-\frac{i}{\hbar}H_o t}$$

That is, $\psi(\vec{r},t)$ is just the field operator we would have at time t if the total Hamiltonian were H_o. It follows in particular that

$$i\hbar\,\frac{\partial\,\psi(\vec{r},t)}{\partial t} = \left[\psi(\vec{r},t),\, H_o\right]$$

$$= \left[-\frac{\hbar^2}{2m}\,\nabla^2 + V(\vec{r}) + W(\vec{r})\right]\psi(\vec{r},t).$$

So $H'_\alpha(t)$ depends on a time-dependent ψ, but the time-dependence is that generated by H_o only. We can calculate this time-dependence exactly. The situation becomes particularly clear and simple if we write

$$\psi(\vec{r},t) = \sum_n \phi_n(\vec{r})\, a_n(t),$$

$$a_n(t) = e^{\frac{i}{\hbar}H_o t}\, a_n\, e^{-\frac{i}{\hbar}H_o t},$$

since then the equation

$$i\hbar\,\frac{\partial\,\psi}{\partial t} = \left[-\frac{h^2}{2m}\,\nabla^2 + V(\vec{r}) + W(\vec{r})\right]\psi$$

becomes

$$\sum_n \phi_n(\vec{r})\, i\hbar \frac{da_n(t)}{dt} = \sum_n E_n \phi_n(\vec{r})\, a_n(t),$$

$$\frac{da_n(t)}{dt} = -i \frac{E_n}{\hbar} a_n(t),$$

$$a_n(t) = a_n e^{-\frac{i}{h} E_n t}.$$

(This result has also been derived earlier for a situation like the present one.) The operators $\psi(\vec{r},t)$, $\psi^+(\vec{r},t)$ which appear in $H'_a(t)$ are then just

$$\psi(\vec{r},t) = \sum_{n=1}^{\infty} \phi_n(\vec{r})\, e^{-\frac{i}{\hbar} E_n t}\, a_n,$$

$$\psi^+(\vec{r},t) = \sum_{n=1}^{\infty} \phi^*_n(\vec{r})\, e^{\frac{i}{\hbar} E_n t}\, a_n^+. \tag{7}$$

The problem of evaluating the expression for ΔE (Equation (5)) is therefore just the problem of calculating the quantities

$$\int_{-\infty}^{t} dt_1 \ldots \int_{-\infty}^{t} dt_n \langle 0| P\left[H'_a(t_1) \ldots H'_a(t_n)\right] |0\rangle$$

with the known expressions for $H'_a(t)$ and $|0\rangle$ in terms of the a_n and a_n^+.

Now in the past we have frequently evaluated expressions of the form

$$\langle 0| \ldots a_i^+ \ldots a_j \ldots a_k^+ \ldots |0\rangle$$

by using the anticommutation relations to rearrange all the operators till creation operators stood to the left and annihilation operators to the right. Exactly this same procedure can be used to evaluate the quantity appearing at the top of the page, in spite of the fact that in this case $|\,0\rangle$ is not the vacuum state but is instead an N-particle ground state. We merely need to notice that since

$$|0\rangle = a_1^+ \; . \; . \; . \; a_N^+ \;|\,\text{Vacuum State}\rangle$$

we have

$$a_i^+ \;|0\rangle = 0, \; i \leq N,$$

but

$$a_i^+ \;|0\rangle \neq 0, \; i > N.$$

Also

$$a_i \;|0\rangle = 0, \; i > N,$$

but

$$a_i \;|\,0\rangle \neq 0, \; i \leq N.$$

These equations indicate that it would be convenient to rename some of our operators in the following fashion. We introduce a set of operators b_i, $i = 1, 2, \ldots, N$, defined as $b_i = a_i^+$, $i = 1, 2, \ldots, N$. Then we also have $b_i^+ = a_i$, $i = 1, 2, \ldots, N$. The preceding equations can be rewritten as

$$b_i \;|0\rangle = a_i^+ \;|0\rangle = 0, \; i \leq N,$$

$$a_i \;|0\rangle = 0, \; i > N,$$

$$b_i^+ \;|0\rangle = a_i \;|0\rangle \neq 0, \; i \leq N,$$

$$a_i^+ \;|0\rangle \neq 0, \; i > N.$$

Now we have arranged things so that nonadjoint operators applied to $|0\rangle$ always give zero. We can interpret the above relations figuratively as follows: since $b_i^+ |0\rangle = a_i |0\rangle$ is an N-1 fermion state, we can say that b_i^+ acting on the ground state $|0\rangle$ creates a "hole" in the i-th state. The operator $b_i = a_i^+$ will create a particle - and so annihilate a hole - in the i-th state. a_i and a_i^+ retain their usual significance as annihilation and creation operators, but now we consider the a's only for $i > N$. That is, the a's create and annihilate particles in states above the surface of the Fermi sea. We can write

$$\psi(\vec{r},t) = \sum_{i=1}^{N} \phi_i(\vec{r})\, e^{-\frac{i}{\hbar}E_i t} a_i + \sum_{i=N+1}^{\infty} \phi_i(\vec{r})\, e^{-\frac{i}{\hbar}E_i t} a_i$$

$$= \sum_{i=1}^{N} \phi_i(\vec{r})\, e^{-\frac{i}{\hbar}E_i t} b_i^+ + \sum_{i=N+1}^{\infty} \phi_i(\vec{r})\, e^{-\frac{i}{\hbar}E_i t} a_i$$

$$= \psi^{(+)}(\vec{r},t) + \psi^{(-)}(\vec{r},t), \tag{8}$$

where $\psi^{(-)}(\vec{r},t)$ annihilates the ground state $|0\rangle$, while $\psi^{(+)}(\vec{r},t)$ applied to the ground state acts as a creation operator for holes. Similarly

$$\psi^+(\vec{r},t) = \sum_{i=1}^{N} \phi_i^*(\vec{r})\, e^{\frac{i}{\hbar}E_i t} b_i + \sum_{i=N+1}^{\infty} \phi_i^*(\vec{r})\, e^{\frac{i}{\hbar}E_i t} a_i^+$$

$$= \psi^{+(-)}(\vec{r},t) + \psi^{+(+)}(\vec{r},t), \tag{9}$$

where $\psi^{+(+)}(\vec{r},t)$ creates an additional particle in an excited state when applied to the ground state, while $\psi^{+(-)}(\vec{r},t)$ annihilates holes. It is important to note that the sign and the adjoint symbol do not commute. In fact,

$$\left[\psi^{(+)}(\vec{r},t)\right]^+ = \psi^{+(-)}(\vec{r},t),$$

$$\left[\psi^{(-)}(\vec{r},t)\right]^+ = \psi^{+(+)}(\vec{r},t).$$

As for the commutation rules, we see that

$$\left[b_i, b_j^+\right]_+ = \left[a_i^+, a_j\right]_+ = \delta_{ij}, \quad i,j \leq N,$$

$$\left[a_i, a_j^+\right]_+ = \delta_{ij}, \quad i,j > N,$$

and all other anticommutators vanish. (For instance,

$$\left[b_i, a_j\right]_+ = \left[a_i^+, a_j\right]_+ = \delta_{ij} = 0, \text{ since } i \leq N \text{ and } j > N.)$$

It follows at once that

$$\left[\psi^{(+)}(\vec{r}, t), \psi^{+(-)}(\vec{r}', t')\right]_+$$

$$= \sum_{i=1}^{N} \sum_{j=1}^{N} \phi_i(\vec{r}) \phi_j^*(\vec{r}') e^{\frac{i}{\hbar}(E_j t' - E_i t)} \left[b_i^+, b_j\right]_+$$

$$= \sum_{i=1}^{N} \phi_i^* (\vec{r}') \phi_i(\vec{r}) e^{\frac{i}{\hbar} E_i (t'-t)}, \tag{10}$$

$$\left[\psi^{(-)}(\vec{r}, t), \psi^{+(+)}(\vec{r}', t')\right]_+$$

$$= \sum_{i=N+1}^{\infty} \phi_i^*(\vec{r}') \phi_i(\vec{r}) e^{\frac{i}{\hbar} E_i (t'-t)}, \tag{11}$$

while

$$\left[\psi^{(-)}(\vec{r}, t), \psi^{+(-)}(\vec{r}', t')\right]_+ = \ldots = 0.$$

The modus operandus for the evaluation of

$$\int_{-\infty}^{t} dt_1 \ldots \int_{-\infty}^{t} dt_n \quad \langle 0 | P \left[H_a'(t_1) \ldots H_a'(t_n)\right] | 0 \rangle$$

should now be clear. We will write the ψ's and ψ^+'s appearing in each $H_a'(t_i)$ in the forms $\psi^{(+)} + \psi^{(-)}$, $\psi^{+(+)} + \psi^{+(-)}$, and then use the anticommutation rules just derived to rearrange the operators so that all "minus" operators stand to the right of all "plus" operators. Evaluation of the matrix element in the integrand is then immediate, since any terms which involve operators after all the commutations are performed give zero. Only the terms which contain a product of functions of the kind

$$\sum_{i=1}^{N} \phi_i^*(\vec{r}') \phi_i(\vec{r})\, e^{\frac{i}{\hbar} E_i (t'-t)},$$

etc., multiplying the expectation value $\langle O|O\rangle = 1$ will give a contribution; so in principle the integrations can then be carried out. Therefore, what we need is a systematic procedure for reducing a product like

$$P\left[H'_a(t_1) \ldots H'_a(t_n)\right]$$

to the form where all annihilation operators stand to the right of all creation operators - the so-called "normal product form".

3. Wick's Theorem

This systematic procedure is yielded by a messy but straightforward theorem called Wick's theorem. Wick's theorem exists in several variants, and we shall begin with the simplest of these. In order to see the principles involved, let us first consider the operator product $\psi^+(x)\,\psi(y)$ (where we now denote by a single symbol x the three spatial coordinates $\vec{r}$ and the time t); and let us suppose that we wish to write this in a form such that all creation operators stand to the left of all annihilation operators. Since

$$\begin{aligned}\psi^+(x)\,\psi(y) &= \left[\psi^{+(+)}(x) + \psi^{+(-)}(x)\right]\left[\psi^{(+)}(y) + \psi^{(-)}(y)\right] \\ &= \psi^{+(+)}(x)\,\psi^{(+)}(y) + \psi^{+(+)}(x)\,\psi^{(-)}(y) \\ &\quad + \psi^{+(-)}(x)\,\psi^{(-)}(y) + \psi^{+(-)}(x)\,\psi^{(+)}(y),\end{aligned}$$

we see that all but the last of the four terms we obtain by writing each operator as a sum of its creation and annihilation parts and carrying out the multiplications is already in the desired form. By using the anticommutation relations we may write this exceptional term as

$$-\psi^{(+)}(y)\,\psi^{+(-)}(x) + \left[\psi^{+(-)}(x), \psi^{(+)}(y)\right]_+,$$

where the anticommutator which appears is just a known c-number function. We shall for convenience introduce the notation

$$\left[\psi^{+(-)}(x),\ \psi^{(+)}(y)\right]_+ = \underbrace{\psi^{+}(x)\ \psi(y)}. \tag{12}$$

With this convention we can write $\psi^{+}(x)\ \psi(y)$ as

$$\psi^{+}(x)\ \psi(y) = :\psi^{+}(x)\ \psi(y): + \underbrace{\psi^{+}(x)\ \psi(y)}, \tag{13}$$

where

$$\begin{aligned} :\psi^{+}(x)\psi(y): = {} & \psi^{+(+)}(x)\ \psi^{(+)}(y) + \psi^{+(+)}(x)\ \psi^{(-)}(y) \\ & -\psi^{(+)}(y)\ \psi^{+(-)}(x) + \psi^{+(-)}(x)\ \psi^{(-)}(y) \end{aligned} \tag{14}$$

is by definition the <u>normal product</u> of $\psi^{+}(x)$ and $\psi(y)$. The result (13) solves our problem of reducing an ordinary operator product to normal product form for this particular case. By the same methods one may see that

$$\psi(x)\psi^{+}(y) = :\psi(x)\ \psi^{+}(y): + \underbrace{\psi(x)\psi^{+}(y)},$$

where

$$\begin{aligned} :\psi(x)\ \psi^{+}(y): = {} & \psi^{(+)}(x)\ \psi^{+(+)}(y) + \psi^{(+)}(x)\ \psi^{+(-)}(y) \\ & -\psi^{+(+)}(y)\ \psi^{(-)}(x) + \psi^{(-)}(x)\ \psi^{+(-)}(y), \end{aligned}$$

$$\underbrace{\psi(x)\ \psi^{+}(y)} = \left[\psi^{(-)}(x),\ \psi^{+(+)}(y)\right]_+ ;$$

and also one verifies immediately that

$$\begin{aligned} \psi(x)\psi(y) = {} & :\psi(x)\ \psi(y): \\ \equiv {} & \psi^{(+)}(x)\psi^{(+)}(y) + \psi^{(+)}(x)\ \psi^{(-)}(y) \\ & - \psi^{(+)}(y)\psi^{(-)}(x) + \psi^{(-)}(x)\psi^{(-)}(y), \end{aligned}$$

with an analogous result for $\psi^{+}(x)\ \psi^{+}(y)$.

These results suggest that it would be useful to make the following definitions. Let $A_1(x_1)$, $A_2(x_2)$, . . . , $A_n(x_n)$ be a set of operators each of which is a creation or an annihilation operator (i.e., it annihilates the ground state when acting to the left or to the right, respectively) or a sum of two such operators; and suppose each creation or annihilation operator involved in the A's has either a c-number commutator or a c-number anticommutator with every other such operator. Then we define the normal product

$$:A_1(x_1) \ldots A_n(x_n):$$

of the operators as follows: write each A_i as a sum of its creation part and its annihilation part and carry out all the multiplications in the product so as to obtain a sum of terms each of which is a product of <u>m</u> creation operators and <u>n-m</u> annihilation operators (for some integer m). In each of these terms interchange the operators (if necessary) to reach a form in which all creation operators stand to the left of all annihilation operators; and then affix a factor $(-1)^P$ to the term, where P is the number of interchanges of fermion operators made in the course of the rearrangement of operators. The sum of all the terms, after each has been altered in this fashion, constitutes by definition the normal product

$$:A_1(x_1) \ldots A_n(x_n):$$

of the operators $A_1(x_1) \ldots A_n(x_n)$. Furthermore, we define the <u>contraction</u> $\underbrace{A_i(x_i)A_j(x_j)}$ of two of the operators as

$$\underbrace{A_i(x_i)\,A_j(x_j)} = A_i(x_i)A_j(x_j) - :A_i(x_i)\,A_j(x_j):$$

Since we have assumed that the operators have commutators or anticommutators which are c-numbers, it is clear that the contraction of two operators will be a c-number.

Note that it follows from our definition that, e.g., if A_1 and A_2 are fermion operators then

$$:A_1(x_1)\,A_2(x_2)\,A_3(x_3) \ldots A_n(x_n):$$

$$= -:A_2(x_2)\,A_1(x_1)\,A_3(x_3) \ldots A_n(x_n):,$$

and so on.

Let us make one further definition, that of the meaning of a <u>contraction within a normal product.</u> By the symbol

$$:\underbrace{A_1 (x_1) A_2 (x_2) A_3}(x_3) A_4 (x_4) \ldots A_n(x_n):$$

we mean

$$(-1)^P \underbrace{A_1 (x_1) A_3}(x_3) \colon A_2 (x_2) A_4 (x_4) \ldots A_n(x_n):,$$

where P is the number of interchanges of fermion operators which is necessary to go from the order

$$A_1 A_2 A_3 A_4 \ldots A_n$$

to the order

$$A_1 A_3 A_2 A_4 \ldots A_n.$$

Similarly

$$:\underbrace{A_1 (x_1) \underbrace{A_2 (x_2) A_3}(x_3) A_4 (x_4) \ldots A_{n-1}(x_{n-1}) A_n}(x_n):$$

$$= (-1)^P \underbrace{A_1 (x_1) A_3}(x_3) \underbrace{A_2 (x_2) A_n}(x_n) \colon A_4 (x_4) \ldots A_{n-1} (x_{n-1}):,$$

where P is the number of interchanges of fermion operators made in going from the order

$$A_1 A_2 A_3 A_4, \ldots A_{n-1} A_n$$

to the order

$$A_1 A_3 A_2 A_n A_4 \ldots A_{n-1},$$

and so on.

We are now in a position to state Wick's theorem, which tells us how to reduce an operator product

$$A_1 (x_1) A_2 (x_2) \ldots A_n (x_n)$$

to the form of a sum of normal products. Specifically, the theorem says the following: when the hypotheses concerning the commutation properties which were stated earlier are satisfied, the operator product

$$A_1 (x_1) A_2 (x_2) \ldots A_n(x_n)$$

is just equal to <u>the sum of normal products with all possible contractions</u> (including the term with none at all). That is

$$A_1(x_1)A_2(x_2)\ldots A_n(x_n) = :A_1(x_1)A_2(x_2)\ldots A_n(x_n): +$$

$$+ :\underbrace{A_1(x_1)A_2}(x_2)A_3(x_3)\ldots A_n(x_n): + :\underbrace{A_1(x_1)A_2(x_2)A_3}(x_3)\ldots A_n(x_n):$$

$$+ \ldots + \text{(all combinations of two contractions at a time)} + \ldots$$

$$+ :\underbrace{A_1(x_1)A_2}(x_2)\underbrace{A_3(x_3)\ldots A_n}(x_n): +$$

$$+ \ldots \text{(all operators - or all but one - contracted in all possible ways).}$$

The proof of this theorem is straightforward, but lack of time prevents our proving it here. Proofs may be found in most books discussing field theory or the use of field-theoretical methods. (A good reference is Brout, R., and P. Carruthers, <u>Lectures on the Many-Electron Problem</u> [Interscience, 1963], pp. 52-53.) The proof for the general case is obtained by induction from the cases

$$A_1(x_1) = :A_1(x_1):,$$

$$A_1(x_1)A_2(x_2) = :A_1(x_1)A_2(x_2): + \underbrace{A_1(x_1)A_2}(x_2).$$

For purposes of concreteness let us write down the statement of the theorem in the case where n = 3 and all the A's are fermion operators. In this situation Wick's theorem says that

$$\begin{aligned} A_1(x_1)A_2(x_2)A_3(x_3) &= :A_1(x_1)A_2(x_2)A_3(x_3): + :\underbrace{A_1(x_1)A_2}(x_2)A_3(x_3): \\ &+ :\underbrace{A_1(x_1)A_2(x_2)A_3}(x_3): + :A_1(x_1)\underbrace{A_2(x_2)A_3}(x_3): \\ &= :A_1(x_1)A_2(x_2)A_3(x_3): + \underbrace{A_1(x_1)A_2}(x_2)A_3(x_3) \\ &- \underbrace{A_1(x_1)A_3}(x_3)A_2(x_2) + \underbrace{A_2(x_2)A_3}(x_3)A_1(x_1). \end{aligned}$$

(Note that in practice we would never actually encounter an operator product consisting of an <u>odd</u> number of fermion operators.)

The theorem which has just been stated is a very useful tool in evaluating ground-state expectation values of operator products. In fact, we see by using Wick's theorem and the properties of the creation and annihilation operators that the only contributions to

$$\langle 0|A_1(x_1)A_2(x_2)\ldots A_n(x_n)|0\rangle$$

come from those terms in which all operators are contracted - since a normal product which still contains operators will have either an annihilation operator standing to the right which gives zero when applied to $|0\rangle$, or a creation operator standing to the left which gives zero when applied to $\langle 0|$, or both. However, the theorem as we have formulated it so far is not directly applicable to an evaluation of the quantities

$$\int_{-\infty}^{t} dt_1 \ldots \int_{-\infty}^{t} dt_n \; P\left[H_a'(t_1) \ldots H_a'(t_n)\right],$$

$$H_a'(t) = e^{-a|t|}\left\{\frac{1}{2}\int d^3x\, d^3x'\, \psi^+(\vec{r},t)\,\psi^+(\vec{r}',t)\,v(\vec{r},\vec{r}')\,\psi(\vec{r}',t)\,\psi(\vec{r},t)\right.$$

$$\left. - \int d^3x\, \psi^+(\vec{r},t)\,W(\vec{r})\,\psi(\vec{r},t)\right\},$$

because the integrand is not an ordinary operator product but a combination of ordinary and of time-ordered operator products. It turns out to be quite simple, though, to find a modification of Wick's theorem which will apply to this case also.

4. Time-Ordered Operator Products

Let us introduce a new time-ordering operation T which is defined as follows: if $A_1(x_1), \ldots, A_n(x_n)$ is a set of time-dependent operators (remember $x_i = (\vec{r}_i, t_i)$), then

$$T\left[A_1(x_1)A_2(x_2)\cdots A_n(x_n)\right] = (-1)^P A_{i_1}(x_{i_1})\,A_{i_2}(x_{i_2})\cdots A_{i_n}(x_{i_n}),$$

where $t_{i_1} > t_{i_2} > \cdots > t_{i_n}$ and P is the number of interchanges of fermion operators required to go from the order

$$A_1 A_2 \ldots A_n$$

to the order

$$A_{i_1} A_{i_2} \ldots A_{i_n}.$$

(Note that T coincides with the operator P introduced earlier in the case where each A is a product of an even number of fermion operators). Let us consider again the simplest case, that of a product of two fermion operators. We have the definition

$$T\left[\psi^+(x)\,\psi(y)\right] = \begin{cases} \psi^+(x)\,\psi(y), & x_0 > y_0 \\ -\psi(y)\,\psi^+(x), & y_0 > x_0 \end{cases},$$

where we have used x_0 to represent the time variable in $x = (\vec{r}, t)$. Now

$$\psi^+(x)\psi(y) = :\psi^+(x)\psi(y): + \underline{\psi^+(x)\psi(y)},$$

$$-\psi(y)\psi^+(x) = -:\psi(y)\psi^+(x): - \underline{\psi(y)\psi^+(x)}$$

$$= :\psi^+(x)\psi(y): - \underline{\psi(y)\psi^+(x)}.$$

Therefore

$$T\left[\psi^+(x)\psi(y)\right] = :\psi^+(x)\psi(y): + \begin{cases} \underline{\psi^+(x)\psi(y)}, & x_0 > y_o \\ -\underline{\psi(y)\psi^+(x)}, & y_0 > x_0. \end{cases}$$

5. Chronological Contractions and Green's Functions

By using the function $\theta(x_0)$ defined as

$$\theta(x_0) = \begin{cases} 1, & x_o > 0 \\ 0, & x_0 < 0 \end{cases}$$

we can write this expression as

$$T\left[\psi^+(x)\psi(y)\right] = :\psi^+(x)\psi(y): + \theta(x_0 - y_0)\underline{\psi^+(x)\psi(y)}$$

$$- \theta(y_0 - x_0)\ \underline{\psi(y)\psi^+(x)}$$

$$= :\psi^+(x)\psi(y): + \overline{\psi^+(x)\psi(y)},$$

where the quantity

$$\overline{\psi^+(x)\psi(y)} \equiv \theta(x_0 - y_0)\underline{\psi^+(x)\psi(y)} - \theta(y_0 - x_0)\underline{\psi(y)\psi^+(x)}$$

is called the "chronological contraction" of $\psi^+(x)$ and $\psi(y)$. Since

$$\underline{\psi^+(x)\psi(y)} = \left[\psi^{+(-)}(x), \psi^{(+)}(y)\right]_+ = \sum_{n=1}^{N} \phi_n^*(\vec{x})\, \phi_n(\vec{y})\, e^{\frac{i}{\hbar}E_n(x_0 - y_o)}$$

$$\underbrace{\psi(y)\psi^{+}}(x) = \left[\psi^{(-)}(y),\, \psi^{+(+)}(x)\right]_{+} = \sum_{n=N+1}^{\infty} \phi_n^{*}(\vec{x})\, \phi_n(\vec{y})\, e^{\frac{i}{\hbar} E_n (x_o - y_o)},$$

we see that

$$\overbrace{\psi^{+}(x)\,\psi(y)} = \theta(x_o - y_o) \sum_{n=1}^{N} \phi_n^{*}(\vec{x})\, \phi_n(\vec{y})\, e^{\frac{i}{\hbar} E_n (x_o - y_o)}$$

$$- \theta(y_o - x_o) \sum_{n=N+1}^{\infty} \phi_n^{*}(\vec{x})\, \phi_n(\vec{y})\, e^{\frac{i}{\hbar} E_n (x_o - y_o)}.$$

It is interesting to note that since

$$\frac{d}{dx_o}\, \theta(x_o - y_o) = - \frac{d}{dx_o}\, \theta(y_o - x_o) = \delta(x_o - y_o)$$

we have

$$\left[i\hbar \frac{\partial}{\partial x_o} - \frac{\hbar^2}{2m} \nabla_x^{2} + V(\vec{x}) + W(\vec{x}) \right] \overbrace{\psi^{+}(x)\,\psi(y)} =$$

$$= i\hbar\, \delta(x_o - y_o) \left(\sum_{n=1}^{N} + \sum_{n=N+1}^{\infty} \right) \phi_n^{*}(\vec{x})\, \phi_n(\vec{y})\, e^{\frac{i}{\hbar} E_n (x_o - y_o)}$$

$$- \theta(x_o - y_o) \sum_{n=1}^{N} E_n\, \phi_n^{*}(\vec{x})\, \phi_n(\vec{y})\, e^{\frac{i}{\hbar} E_n (x_o - y_o)} \quad \left(\text{from } \frac{\partial}{\partial x_o}\right)$$

$$+ \theta(x_o - y_o) \sum_{n=1}^{N} E_n\, \phi_n^{*}(\vec{x})\, \phi_n(\vec{y})\, e^{\frac{i}{\hbar} E_n (x_o - y_o)} \quad (\text{from the } \vec{x} \text{ part})$$

$$+ \theta(x_o - y_o) \sum_{n=N+1}^{\infty} E_n\, \phi_n^{*}(\vec{x})\, \phi_n(\vec{y})\, e^{\frac{i}{\hbar} E_n (x_o - y_o)} \quad \left(\text{from } \frac{\partial}{\partial x_o}\right)$$

$$- \theta(x_o - y_o) \sum_{n=N+1}^{\infty} E_n\, \phi_n^{*}(\vec{x})\, \phi_n(\vec{y})\, e^{\frac{i}{\hbar} E_n (x_o - y_o)} \quad (\text{from the } \vec{x} \text{ part})$$

$$= i\hbar\, \delta(x_o - y_o) \sum_{n=1}^{\infty} \phi_n^{*}(\vec{x})\, \phi_n(\vec{y})\, e^{\frac{i}{\hbar} E_n (x_o - y_o)}$$

$$= i\hbar\, \delta(x_o - y_o) \sum_{n=1}^{\infty} \phi_n^{*}(\vec{x})\, \phi_n(\vec{y})$$

(since the product is zero unless $x_o = y_o$)

$$= i\hbar\,\delta(x_o - y_o)\,\delta(\vec{x} - \vec{y})$$

(because the set of functions ϕ_n is complete).

For this reason the chronological contraction can be called a <u>Green's function</u>.

In the same way as above we can define $\overbrace{\psi(x)\;\psi^{+}}(y)$ by the relation

$$T\left[\psi(x)\psi^{+}(y)\right] = \;:\psi(x)\,\psi^{+}(y): \; + \; \overbrace{\psi(x)\psi^{+}}(y).$$

Since

$$T\left[\psi(x)\,\psi^{+}(y)\right] = \begin{cases} \psi(x)\psi^{+}(y), & x_o > y_o \\ -\,\psi^{+}(y)\,\psi(x), & y_o > x_o \end{cases},$$

we see that

$$T\left[\psi^{+}(y)\psi(x)\right] = \begin{Bmatrix} \psi^{+}(y)\psi(x), & y_o > x_o \\ -\psi(x)\psi^{+}(y), & x_o > y_o \end{Bmatrix} = -\,T\left[\psi(x)\psi^{+}(y)\right]$$

and

$$T\left[\psi(x)\psi^{+}(y)\right] = \;:\psi(x)\psi^{+}(y): \; + \; \overbrace{\psi(x)\psi^{+}}(y)$$

$$= -\,T\left[\psi^{+}(y)\psi(x)\right] = -\,:\psi^{+}(y)\psi(x): - \;\overbrace{\psi^{+}(y)\psi}(x)$$

$$= \;:\psi(x)\psi^{+}(y): - \;\overbrace{\psi^{+}(y)\psi}(x)\,.$$

Thus it is seen that

$$\overbrace{\psi(x)\psi^{+}}(y) = -\,\overbrace{\psi^{+}(y)\psi}(x)$$

$$= -\,\theta(y_o - x_o)\sum_{n=1}^{N} \phi_n^{*}(\vec{y})\,\phi_n(\vec{x})\,e^{\frac{i}{\hbar}E_n(y_o - x_o)}$$

$$+ \ \theta(x_o - y_o) \sum_{n=N+1}^{\infty} \phi_n^*(\vec{y})\, \phi_n(\vec{x})\, e^{\frac{i}{\hbar} E_n (y_o - x_o)} \ .$$

One also sees at once that

$$T\left[\psi(x)\psi(y)\right] = \begin{cases} \psi(x)\psi(y), & x_o > y_o \\ -\psi(y)\psi(x), & y_o > x_o \end{cases}$$

$$= \psi(x)\psi(y) = :\psi(x)\psi(y): \quad .$$

That is, $\overbrace{\psi(x)\psi(y)} = 0$. Similar statements apply to ψ^+.

We now have the following result: if $A_1(x_1)$ and $A_2(x_2)$ are any two operators which have either a c-number commutator or a c-number anticommutator with one another, then there exists a c-number function $\overbrace{A_1(x_1)\, A_2}(x_2)$, the "chronological contraction" of the operators, which is such that

$$T\left[A_1(x_1)A_2(x_2)\right] = :A_1(x_1)A_2(x_2): + \overbrace{A_1(x_1)A_2}(x_2).$$

Since also (trivially)

$$T\left[A_1(x_1)\right] = A_1(x_1) = :A_1(x_1):,$$

it is clear that the same induction proof as mentioned in the case of the product $A_1(x_1) \ldots A_n(x_n)$ will now lead to the following result: the time-ordered operator product

$$T\left[A_1(x_1)A_2(x_2) \ldots A_n(x_n)\right]$$

is equal to the sum of the normal products with all possible <u>chronological</u> <u>contractions</u>:

$$T\left[A_1(x_1)A_2(x_2) \ldots A_n(x_n)\right] = :A_1(x_1)A_2(x_2) \ldots A_n(x_n):$$

$$+ \ :\overbrace{A_1(x_1)A_2}(x_2) \ldots A_n(x_n): + \ldots \quad .$$

This theorem, together with the Wick's theorem for ordinary operator products, will allow us to evaluate all the terms

$$\int_{\infty}^{t} dt_1 \dots \int_{\infty}^{t} dt_n \langle O \,|\, P\left[H_a'(t_1)\dots H_a'(t_n)\right] |O\rangle$$

in a straightforward fashion.

In fact, let us actually carry out the evaluation of the first one or two terms of the sort given above. Our series is

$$\langle O \,|\, O\rangle + \left(-\frac{i}{\hbar}\right)\int_{-\infty}^{t} dt_1 \,\langle O|P\left[H_a'(t_1)\right]|O\rangle +$$

$$+\frac{1}{2!}\left(-\frac{i}{\hbar}\right)^2 \int_{-\infty}^{t} dt_1 \int_{-\infty}^{t} dt_2 \,\langle O|P\left[H_a'(t_1)\,H_a'(t_2)\right]|O\rangle + \dots \,.$$

The time-ordering in the first non-constant term is trivial. To evaluate the term we must simply obtain an expression for

$$e^{-a|t|}\Big\{\tfrac{1}{2}\int d^3x\, d^3x' \,\langle O|\,\psi^+(\vec r,t)\,\psi^+(\vec r',t)\,v(\vec r,\vec r')\,\psi(\vec r',t)\psi(\vec r,t)|O\rangle$$

$$-\int d^3x \,\langle O|\,\psi^+(\vec r,t)\,W(\vec r)\,\psi(\vec r,t)\,|O\rangle\Big\}.$$

Wick's theorem for ordinary operator products shows that

$$\psi^+(\vec r,t)\psi(\vec r,t) = \;:\psi^+(\vec r,t)\psi(\vec r,t): + \;\underbrace{\psi^+(\vec r,t)\psi(\vec r,t)} \qquad (15)$$

and

$$\psi^+(\vec r,t)\psi^+(\vec r',t)\psi(\vec r',t)\psi(\vec r,t) = \;:\psi^+(\vec r,t)\,\psi^+(\vec r',t)\psi(\vec r',t)\,\psi(\vec r,t):$$

$$+:\underbrace{\psi^+(\vec r,t)\,\psi^+(\vec r',t)\psi(\vec r',t)}\,\psi(\vec r,t): + \;:\underbrace{\psi^+(\vec r,t)\psi^+(\vec r',t)\psi(\vec r',t)\psi(\vec r,t)}:$$

$$+:\psi^+(\vec r,t)\,\underbrace{\psi^+(\vec r',t)\psi(\vec r',t)}\psi(\vec r,t): + \;:\psi^+(\vec r,t)\underbrace{\psi^+(\vec r',t)\psi(\vec r',t)\psi(\vec r,t)}: \qquad (1$$

$$+:\underbrace{\psi^+(\vec r,t)\psi^+(\vec r',t)\psi(\vec r',t)}\psi(\vec r,t): + \;:\underbrace{\psi^+(\vec r,t)\underbrace{\psi^+(\vec r',t)\psi(\vec r',t)}\psi(\vec r,t)}: \,.$$

It is seen that the expansion of the operator products in terms of normal products is rather messy. Actually, in the expressions written above only three terms will make a contribution to

$$\int_{-\infty}^{t} dt_1 \quad \langle 0 | H_a' (t_1) | O \rangle,$$

the one term in (15) and the two terms in (16) in which all of the operators are contracted. If we recall that

$$\underbrace{\psi^+(\vec{r}, t)\psi}(\vec{r}', t) = \sum_{n=1}^{N} \phi_n^* (\vec{r}) \phi_n (\vec{r}'),$$

and if we make the definitions

$$\rho (\vec{r}) = \sum_{n=1}^{N} \phi_n^* (\vec{r}) \phi_n(\vec{r}),$$

$$\rho (\vec{r}, \vec{r}') = \sum_{n=1}^{N} \phi_n^* (\vec{r}) \phi_n (\vec{r}'),$$

then we see that the fully-contracted parts of (15) and (16) are

$$\underbrace{\psi^+ (\vec{r}, t)\psi}(\vec{r}, t) = \rho (\vec{r})$$

and

$$: \psi^+ (\vec{r}, t)\psi^+ (\vec{r}', t) \; \psi(\vec{r}', t)\psi (\vec{r}, t): + \; : \psi^+(\vec{r}, t)\psi^+(\vec{r}', t)\psi(\vec{r}', t)\psi (\vec{r}, t):$$

$$= -\underbrace{\psi^+ (\vec{r}, t)\psi}(\vec{r}', t)\underbrace{\psi^+(\vec{r}', t)\psi}(\vec{r}, t) + \underbrace{\psi^+(\vec{r}, t)\psi}(\vec{r}, t)\underbrace{\psi^+(\vec{r}', t)\psi}(\vec{r}', t) =$$

$$= - \rho (\vec{r},\vec{r}') \rho (\vec{r}', \vec{r}) + \rho (\vec{r})\rho (\vec{r}'),$$

respectively. The term

$$\left(-\frac{i}{\hbar}\right) \int_{-\infty}^{t} dt_1 \quad \langle 0 | H_a' (t_1) | O \rangle$$

is therefore just

$$\left(-\frac{i}{\hbar}\right)\int_{-\infty}^{t} dt_1 \; e^{-a|t_1|}\left\{\frac{1}{2}\int d^3 x \, d^3 x' \langle 0|\psi^+(\vec{r}, t_1)\psi^+(\vec{r}', t_1) v(\vec{r}, \vec{r}')\psi(\vec{r}', t_1)\psi(\vec{r},t_1) |O\rangle\right.$$

$$-\int d^3x \ \langle 0|\psi^+(\vec{r},t_1)\, W(\vec{r})\, \psi(\vec{r},t_1)|0\rangle\Big\}$$

$$= \left(-\frac{i}{\hbar}\right)\int_{-\infty}^{t} dt_1\, e^{-a|t_1|}\Big\{\tfrac{1}{2}\int d^3x\, d^3x'\, v(\vec{r},\vec{r}')\left[\rho(\vec{r})\rho(\vec{r}') - \rho(\vec{r},\vec{r}')\rho(\vec{r}',\vec{r})\right]$$

$$-\int d^3x\ \rho(\vec{r})\, W(\vec{r})\Big\}$$

$$= \left(-\frac{i}{\hbar}\right)\frac{e^{at}}{a}\Big[\sum_{n=1}^{N}\sum_{n'=1}^{N}\tfrac{1}{2}\int d^3x\, d^3x'\, \phi_n^*(\vec{r})\phi_{n'}^*(\vec{r}')v(\vec{r},\vec{r}')\phi_{n'}(\vec{r}')\phi_n(\vec{r})$$

$$-\sum_{n=1}^{N}\sum_{n'=1}^{N}\tfrac{1}{2}\int d^3x\, d^3x'\, \phi_n^*(\vec{r})\,\phi_{n'}^*(\vec{r}')\, v(\vec{r},\vec{r}')\,\phi_n(\vec{r}')\phi_{n'}(\vec{r})$$

$$-\sum_{n=1}^{N}\int d^3x\ \phi_n^*(\vec{r})\, W(\vec{r})\, \phi_n(\vec{r})\Big] \qquad (t \leq 0).$$

To get the contribution of this term to the expression for the exact ground state energy we must operate on it with $i\hbar\frac{\partial}{\partial t}$ and set $t = 0$. This just leaves the bracket term itself,

$$\sum_{n=1}^{N}\sum_{n'=1}^{N}\tfrac{1}{2}\int d^3x\, d^3x'\, \phi_n^*(\vec{r})\,\phi_{n'}^*(\vec{r}')\, v(\vec{r},\vec{r}')\,\phi_{n'}(\vec{r}')\,\phi_n(\vec{r}) -$$

$$-\sum_{n=1}^{N}\sum_{n'=1}^{N}\tfrac{1}{2}\int d^3x\, d^3x'\, \phi_n^*(\vec{r})\,\phi_{n'}^*(\vec{r}')\, v(\vec{r},\vec{r}')\phi_n(\vec{r}')\,\phi_{n'}(\vec{r}) -$$

$$-\sum_{n=1}^{N}\int d^3x\ \phi_n^*(\vec{r})\, W(\vec{r})\, \phi_n(\vec{r}).$$

The first and third terms are just the analogues for the present case of the expectation value of the perturbing Hamiltonian in the unperturbed ground state. The second term is the "exchange term", which gives a correction to the expectation value due to the antisymmetric nature of the electron state vectors. The first-order contribution to the energy is therefore exactly what we would expect - but we might have had trouble in guessing this form!

Let us consider the second non-constant term in our perturbation expansion. This is the term

$$\frac{1}{2!}\left(-\frac{i}{\hbar}\right)^2 \int_{-\infty}^{t} dt_1 \int_{-\infty}^{t} dt_2 \quad \langle 0| \; P\left[H_a'(t_1)\, H_a'(t_2)\right] |0\rangle =$$

$$= \frac{1}{2!}\left(-\frac{i}{\hbar}\right)^2 \int_{-\infty}^{t} dt_1 \int_{-\infty}^{t} dt_2 \; e^{-a(|t_1|+|t_2|)} \,.$$

$$\cdot \langle 0|T \Big\{ \Big[\frac{1}{2}\int d^3x' d^3x'' \; \psi^+(\vec{x}', t_1)\psi^+(\vec{x}'', t_1)\; v(\vec{x}', \vec{x}'')\psi(\vec{x}'', t_1)\; \psi(\vec{x}', t_1) -$$

$$- \int d^3x \; \psi^+(\vec{x}, t_1)\; W(\vec{x})\; \psi(\vec{x}, t_1) \Big] \cdot$$

$$\cdot \Big[\frac{1}{2}\int d^3y' \, d^3y'' \; \psi^+(\vec{y}', t_2)\, \psi^+(\vec{y}'', t_2)\, v(\vec{y}', \vec{y}'')\; \psi(\vec{y}'', t_2)\psi(\vec{y}', t_2) -$$

$$- \int d^3y \; \psi^+(\vec{y}, t_2)\; W(\vec{y})\; \psi(\vec{y}, t_2) \Big] \Big\} |0\rangle \,.$$

To evaluate this contribution to ΔE we may proceed in the following fashion. First we express each one of the quantities $H_a'(t_1)$ and $H_a'(t_2)$ as the sum of several terms each of which is in normal product form (using Eqs. (15) and (16), just as we did in the evaluation of the first-order contribution). Then we multiply out the resulting sums so as to get a series of terms each of which is a product of a normal product of operators containing $\vec{x}$'s and t_1 and a normal product of operators containing $\vec{y}$'s and t_2. For instance, one such operator term we would obtain in this fashion is

$$T\Big[: \psi^+(\vec{x}', t_1)\; \psi^+(\vec{x}'', t_1)\; \psi(\vec{x}'', t_1)\; \psi(\vec{x}', t_1): \quad \times$$

$$\times \; : \psi^+(\vec{y}', t_2)\; \underbrace{\psi^+(\vec{y}'', t_2)\; \psi}(\vec{y}'', t_2)\; \psi(\vec{y}', t_2): \Big] \,.$$

We can then apply Wick's theorem for time-ordered products of operators to each of these terms in order to reduce it to complete normal-product form. In this process one point deserves special note, however; since the operators depending on the time variable t_i are already in normal product form with respect to one another, no two of these operators have to be exchanged with one another in reducing a time-ordered product of the above form to normal-product form. It is easy to see that in terms of Wick's theorem this means simply that the operator is equal to the sum of normal products with all possible chronological contractions between pairs of operators with <u>different time variables</u>.

In the expansion of the operator product given on the preceding page, for instance, the term

$$: \psi^{+}(\vec{x}', t_1)\psi^{+}(\vec{x}'', t_1)\psi(\vec{x}'', t_1)\overbrace{\psi(\vec{x}', t_1)\psi^{+}(\vec{y}', t_2)}\underbrace{\psi^{+}(\vec{y}'', t_2)\psi(\vec{y}'', t_2)}\psi(\vec{y}', t_1$$

would appear, but not the term

$$: \psi^{+}(\vec{x}', t_1)\overbrace{\psi^{+}(\vec{x}'', t_1)\psi(\vec{x}'', t_1)}\psi(\vec{x}', t_1)\psi^{+}(\vec{y}', t_2)\underbrace{\psi^{+}(\vec{y}'', t_2)\psi(\vec{y}'', t_2)}\psi(\vec{y}', t_2$$

(In fact, the chronological contraction of two operators with the same time argument is not even defined by the expression previously given - because of the discontinuity of the θ-functions at $t = t'$ - even though it would be very easy to define it for two operators evaluated at the same time in a fashion which would be consistent with the above formalism.)

The procedure described above is straightforward enough, but the expressions obtained in this fashion become rather cumbersome. In fact, just to write down all the terms involved in the expansion of

$$T\left[H_a'(t_1)\,H_a'(t_2)\right]$$

as a sum of normal products would take several pages. Not only is this true because a great many different sorts of contractions are possible when so many operators are involved, but also because in terms which still involve operators - e.g., in a term involving $:\psi^{+}(\vec{y}, t_2)\cdot\psi(\vec{x}; t_1):$ - we must replace each operator by the sum of its positive and negative parts and carry out the multiplications; so each such term when reduced to its simplest form becomes a sum of four, eight, sixteen, or more terms (depending on how many uncontracted operators remain). (Of course, in the present case it has already been pointed out that terms which still contain operators after reduction to normal product form has been made give no contribution. However, in the calculation of some quantities other than the ground state energy such terms are important and must be considered.) Because of the cumbersomeness and complexity of this expansion it is very desirable to have a notation which will allow us to see clearly what terms arise in the reduction of our time-ordered products to normal products, and which will also allow us to evaluate the contributions of these terms without ev having to write down the formal result of the application of Wick's theorem in its tediously-long explicit form.

6. Goldstone Diagrams

Fortunately, it is very easy to devise a notation which will satisfy these needs, and which also gives a useful intuitive picture of the nature of the physical processes which produce the contributions of the various terms. This notation involves the use of figures called diagrams (sometimes "Goldstone diagrams", and in the relativistic case "Feynman diagrams") in which arrows, dotted lines, and points are used to represent various quantities which appear in the expansions of the time-ordered operator products which are obtained by use of Wick's theorem. The symbols and their meanings are as follows:

1. With every coordinate x we associate a point labeled with the symbol x and called a vertex.

$$\cdot\; x$$

When x and x' have the same time argument because they arise from the single term

$$\int d^3 x\, d^3 x'\, \psi^+(x)\, \psi^+(x')\, v(\vec{x}, \vec{x}')\, \psi(x')\, \psi(x)$$

then we place them on the same horizontal line:

$$x\cdot \qquad \cdot x' \,.$$

Coordinates with different time arguments are put on different horizontal lines:

$$y\cdot \qquad \cdot y'$$

$$x\cdot \qquad \cdot x' \,.$$

2. With the operators $\psi^{+(+)}(x)$, $\psi^{+(-)}(x)$, $\psi^{(+)}(x)$, $\psi^{(-)}(x)$ we associate arrows directed into or out of the vertex x as follows:

$\psi^{+(+)}(x)$ 

(particle creation)

$\psi^{+(-)}(x)$ 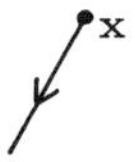

(hole annihilation)

$\psi^{(+)}(x)$ 

(hole creation)

$\psi^{(-)}(x)$ 

(particle annihilation).

Note that the arrows for (+) operators lie <u>above</u> the vertex, those for (-) operators lie <u>below</u>. Also arrows associated with the two components of ψ point <u>toward</u> the vertex, those associated with ψ^+ point <u>away</u> from it.

3. To the function $v(\vec{r}, \vec{r}\,')$ we assign a dotted line connecting the vertices x and x'.

x ---------- x'

With the function $W(\vec{r})$ we associate a dotted horizontal line from the vertex x to a cross-mark.

x ---------- X

4. To the ordinary contraction $\underbrace{\psi^+(x)\,\psi(x')}$ we assign an arrow from x to x'

if x and x' are different, or the simple loop

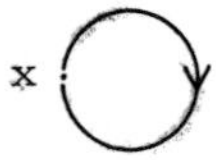

if they are the same. In the latter case we can omit the arrowhead on the line. (Note that in either case $x_o = x'_o$, or the ordinary contraction of the two operators would not appear.)

5. To the chronological contraction $\overbrace{\psi(x)\,\psi^+}(y)$ we assign an arrow directed from y to x:

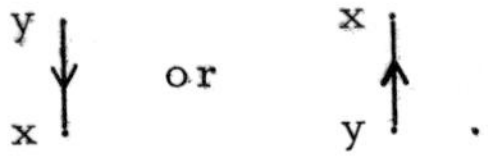

By using these symbols we can represent any of the terms arising in $H_a'(t_1)$, $P\left[H_a'(t_1)H_a'(t_2)\right]$, etc. For instance, the quantity

$$:\underbrace{\psi^+(x)\psi^{+(+)}}(x')\psi(x')\psi^{(-)}(x):\ v(\vec{r}, \vec{r}\,')$$

which appears in the reduction of $H_a'(t_1)$ to normal form just becomes, in diagram form,

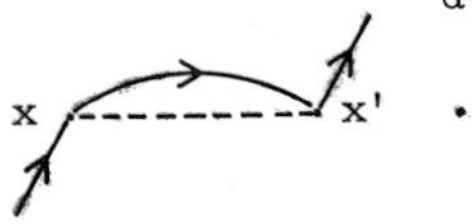

Similarly, the quantity

$$:\psi^{+(+)}(y)\overbrace{\psi(y)\psi^{+(-)}(x')\psi^{+}}(x'')\psi^{(-)}(x'')\psi^{(+)}(x'):\ v(\vec{x}', \vec{x}'')\ W(\vec{y})$$

is represented by the diagram

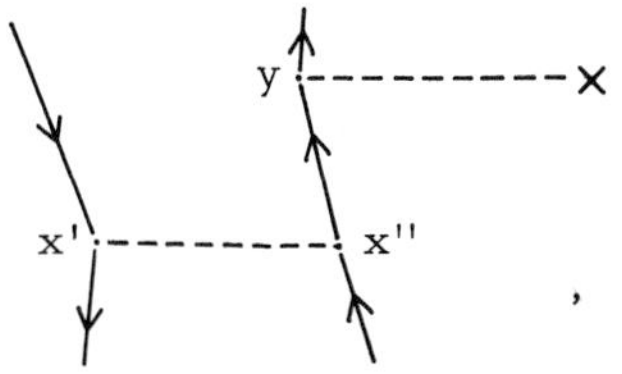

,

and so on.

The important point about diagrams, though, is not that we can draw a diagram for each term in

$$T\left[H_a'(t_1)\ldots H_a'(t_n)\right]$$

but that - provided we follow certain simple rules - we can also <u>find</u> all the terms in

$$T\left[H_a'(t_1)\ldots H_a'(t_n)\right]$$

by drawing all the diagrams of appropriate types. Furthermore, one can with a little practice write down the contribution of the term corresponding to a diagram just by looking at the diagram itself, without even writing down the associated operator form at all. This greatly facilitates the task of computation.

The procedure is as follows. In an n-th order term

$$T\left[H_a'(t_1)\ldots H_a'(t_n)\right]$$

there are n different time variables, one for each H_a'. In every diagram obtained from this term there will be vertices on n different vertical levels (by the rules previously given). Since our H_a' contains both one-particle and two-particle forces, there will be one vertex on the i-th level in some diagrams and two vertices in others (depending on whether

$$\psi^{+}(x_i)W(\vec{x}_i)\psi(x_i) \qquad \text{or} \qquad \psi^{+}(x_i')\psi^{+}(x_i'')\, v(\vec{x}_i', \vec{x}_i'')\psi(x_i'')\psi(x_i')$$

appears as a factor when the multiplications in the product

$$H_a'(t_1). \ . \ . H_a'(t_n)$$

are carried out). All such possibilities must be drawn. For instance, in the case n = 2 we would have the four possibilities

$$\begin{pmatrix} x_2' \cdot & \cdot x_2'' \\ x_1' \cdot & \cdot x_1'' \end{pmatrix}, \quad \begin{pmatrix} & \cdot x_2 \\ x_1' \cdot & \cdot x_1'' \end{pmatrix}, \quad \begin{pmatrix} x_2' \cdot & \cdot x_2'' \\ & \cdot x_1 \end{pmatrix}, \quad \begin{pmatrix} \cdot x_2 \\ \cdot x_1 \end{pmatrix}.$$

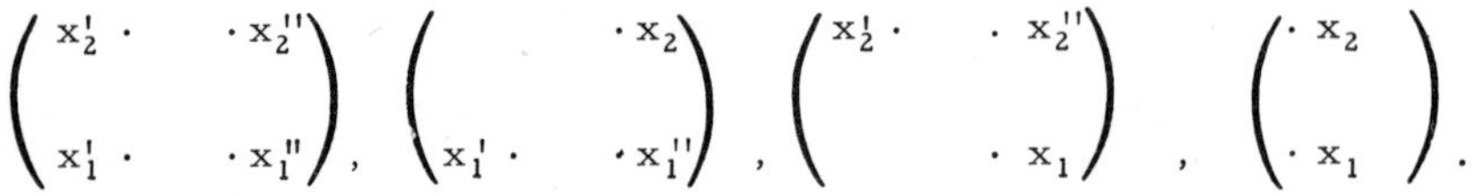

In each diagram of this type one must at each level draw the dotted line representing $v(\vec{x_i'}, \vec{x_i''})$ or $w(\vec{x_i})$, whichever is appropriate. Finally, one draws in arrows in every possible way which gives one arrow going into and one arrow coming out of every vertex. It can immediately be seen from Wick's theorem that the set of diagrams constructed in this way is in one-to-one correspondence with the set of terms obtained by expanding $T\left[H_a'(t_1). \ . \ . H_a'(t_n)\right]$ as a sum of normal products.

Let us consider some examples. In the case n = 1 there are the two sorts of diagrams:

The possibilities obtained by our rules are then

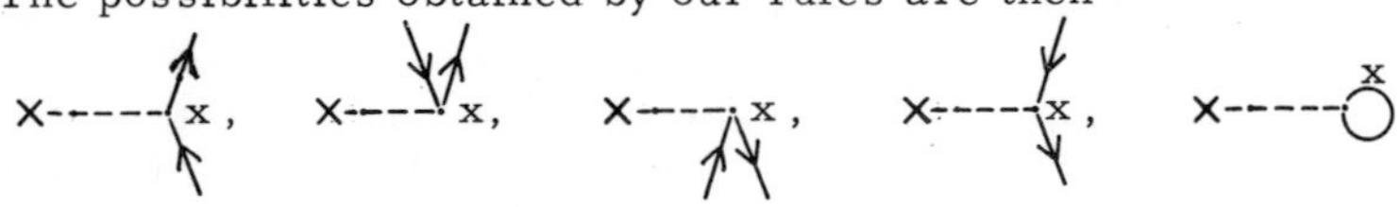

in the first case; and in the second case

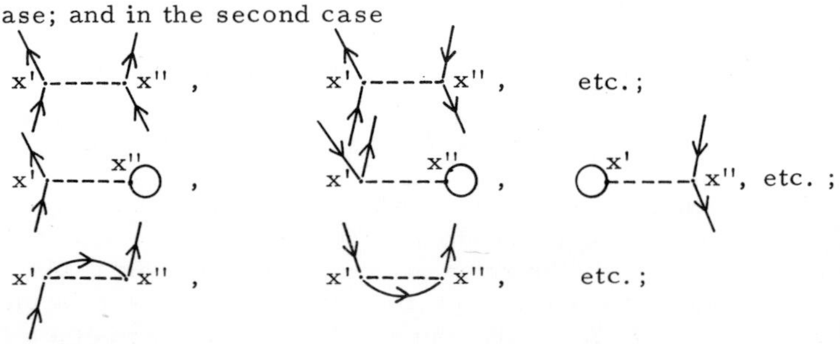

and

Of these diagrams only three actually contribute to ΔE, the three given by

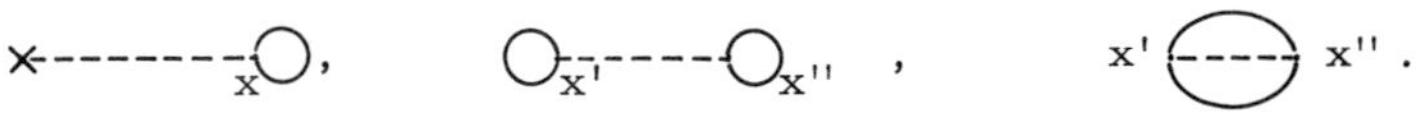

All the other diagrams contain arrows which go off the edge of the diagram, or "external lines" (one such diagram, for instance, is

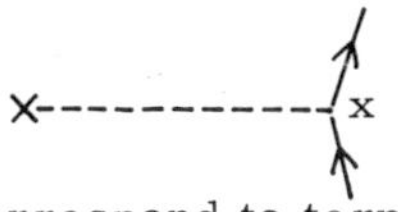

),

and such diagrams correspond to terms which still contain operators in normal-product form and so have zero ground-state expectation value. In general, in any order only diagrams with no external lines give contributions to the expression for ΔE.

As one final example, let us write down a few of the second-order diagrams which contribute to ΔE and show how in a particular case we may write down the explicit expression for the corresponding contribution. As stated earlier, second-order diagrams are of the four types

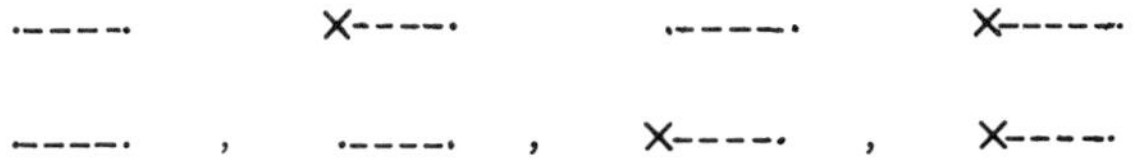

The diagrams of the first type with no external lines include

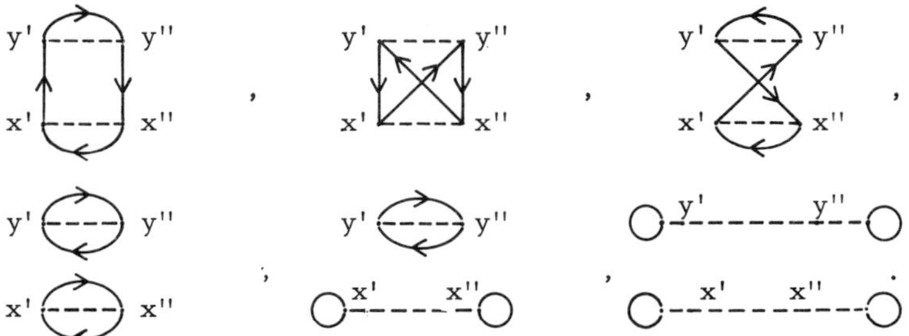

The term in the expansion of $T\left[H_a'(t_1)\,H_a'(t_2)\right]$ corresponding to, for instance,

is that given by the expression

$$\frac{1}{2!}\left(-\frac{i}{\hbar}\right)^2 \int_{-\infty}^{t} dt_1 \int_{-\infty}^{t} dt_2 \; e^{-\alpha(|t_1| + |t_2|)} \cdot$$

$$\cdot \int d^3x' \, d^3x'' \, d^3y' \, d^3y'' \; v(\vec{x'}, \vec{x''}) \, v(\vec{y'}, \vec{y''}) \cdot$$

$$\cdot \; :\psi^+(y')\psi^+(y'')\psi(y'')\psi(y')\psi^+(x')\psi^+(x'')\psi(x'')\psi(x'):$$

$$= \frac{1}{2!}\left(-\frac{i}{\hbar}\right)^2 \int_{-\infty}^{t} dt_1 \int_{-\infty}^{t} dt_2 \; e^{-\alpha(|t_1| + |t_2|)} \cdot$$

$$\cdot \int d^3x' \, d^3x'' \, d^3y' \, d^3y'' \; v(\vec{x'}, \vec{x''}) \, v(\vec{y'}, \vec{y''}) \cdot$$

$$\cdot \; (-1)^{13} \quad \overline{\psi(x')\psi^+(y')} \; \overline{\psi(x'')\psi^+(y'')} \; \overline{\psi(y'')\psi^+(x')} \; \overline{\psi(y')\psi^+(x'')} .$$

Thus it is written explicitly as an integral involving known (in principle!) functions.

Finally, let us add a few comments concerning the "physical" interpretation of the diagrams. (It is uncertain whether the interpretation to be given is <u>really</u> physical, since it depends on the sort of perturbation-theory calculation which is used.) One may, if one wishes, suppose that the diagrams represent actual physical processes, and that these processes are responsible for the energy shift represented by the diagram. For instance, the diagram

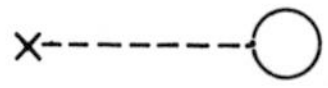

represents a particle interacting with the external potential while staying in the same state, while the diagram

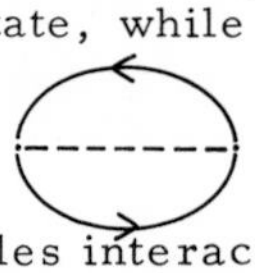

represents two particles interacting by means of the two-body potential and changing places. The diagram

corresponds to two particles interacting via the two-body potential and scattering into excited states, where they again interact and fall back into their original states. An analogous interpretation applies to the diagram

 ,

except that here the particles exchange places in falling back into the original states. Similar interpretations apply to the other diagrams.

We must stop our discussion here for lack of time, in spite of the fact that we have barely begun our study of the theory and applications of this method of time-dependent perturbation theory. It is particularly unfortunate that we have had to omit the derivation of the "linked cluster" expansion theorem, which states that in the expansion of the expression for ΔE the denominator just cancels a corresponding quantity in the numerator so that the value of the series is just equal to the sum of the contributions of all "linked diagrams" only. That is, we do not need to add in the contribution of diagrams like

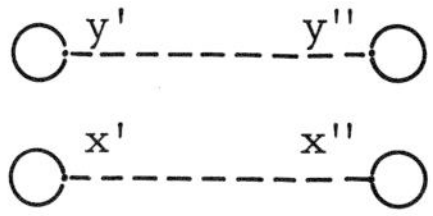

which fall naturally into two separate pieces, but only the contribution of diagrams like

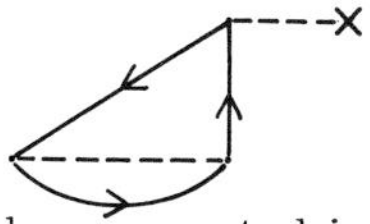

which cannot be separated into two pieces without cutting some lines. A good reference for information about this and many other topics in the subject is the excellent book by Brout and Carruthers which was mentioned earlier.

CLASSICAL FIELDS AND GRAVITATION

by

VITALIJ GARBER*

and

C. A. COULTER,** Editor

*Advanced Systems Laboratory
**Physical Sciences Laboratory
Directorate of Research and Development
U. S. Army Missile Command
Redstone Arsenal, Alabama 35809

ABSTRACT

Graduate-level lectures given at the 1964 Summer Seminar in Theoretical Physics at Redstone Arsenal are presented. This report deals with classical field theory and gravitation. The discussion begins with consideration of the Lagrangian formalism in four-dimensional space-time. Hamilton's principle is applied to obtain the Euler-Lagrange equations of motion. Criteria for Lorentz covariance are developed. Treatment of interacting fields by use of the Lagrangian formulation is illustrated by the consideration of charged particles in an electromagnetic field. Noether's theorem and its connection with conservation laws are outlined, and the application to the particular case of ortochronous Lorentz transformations is described.

Following a review of gravitational experiments supporting the general theory of relativity, the concepts of gravitational and inertial mass equivalence, general covariance, the metric tensor, Riemannian space, and covariant differentiation are developed. The Bianchi identities are derived from the symmetry properties of the affine connection in the Riemannian metric space. Subsequently, gravitational field equations for gravitational fields only and in the presence of other fields are derived. The necessity for explicitly introducing an interaction term in the conventional and quantum mechanical theory is contrasted with the automatic, implicit interaction found in the gravitational field theory. Exact solutions are obtained for the spherically-symmetric Schwarzschild case. The approximate theory for the weak field case is discussed.

TABLE OF CONTENTS

Section I. THE LAGRANGIAN FORMALISM AND THE CLASSICAL THEORY OF FIELDS

1. The Calculus of Variations and Hamilton's Principle

The purely mathematical fundamental problem of the calculus of variations in parametric form considers an integral taken along arcs:[1]

$$I = \int_{t_1}^{t_2} f(u_i, u_i', u_i'', \ldots, t)\, dt, \tag{1}$$

$$u_i(t) : t_i \le t \le t_2, \quad i = 1, \ldots, n;$$

and the problem is to find in the class of admissible arcs joining two fixed points at t_1 and t_2 one which minimizes the integral I. We shall be using the techniques of the calculus of variations in the following discussion. However, we shall not need to consider the general form of the problem as stated above. Rather, we can introduce certain simplifications. Our physical theories will be required to be independent under translations of the origin of our parameter t, i.e., under the transformation

$$t \rightarrow \tau = t + c\ ; \tag{2}$$

therefore, in problems of physical interest the variable t must not appear explicitly in the integrand.[2] We shall also make use of the fact that by substituting new variables for the higher derivatives u_i'', u_i''', etc., one can obtain equivalent equations which must be satisfied by our extremal arcs (the Euler-Lagrange equations) except in a space of more variables. So for our purposes it will be sufficient to consider only integrals of the form:

$$I = \int_{t_1}^{t_2} f(u_i, u_i')\, dt. \tag{3}$$

In our physical theory this is equivalent to the "principle of simplicity" when we take $f(u_i, u_i')$ to be our Lagrangian $L(u_i, u_i')$.

To get the conditions for which our arc $u_i(t)$ will be an extremal (an extremal is an arc along which our integral will have a stationary value or be an extremum), we assume an arbitrary variation which vanishes at the end points:

$$u_i(t) \rightarrow u_i(t) + \alpha_i \eta_i(t),$$
$$\eta_i(t_1) = \eta_i(t_2) = 0, \tag{4}$$

where α_i is some arbitrary constant parameter. Thus we shall consider the quantity

$$I(\alpha_i) = \int_{t_1}^{t_2} f(u_i + \alpha_i \eta_i, u_i' + \alpha_i \eta_i') \, dt. \tag{5}$$

Now a necessary condition that the integral I give a minimum, and a necessary and sufficient condition for I to have a stationary value, is that

$$\left.\frac{\partial I(\alpha_j)}{\partial \alpha_i}\right|_{\alpha_j = 0} = 0, \; i, j = 1, \ldots n. \tag{6}$$

Or, in a more familiar notation, we require that

$$\delta \int_{t_1}^{t_2} f(u_i, u_i') \, dt = 0,$$

$$\left.\frac{\partial}{\partial \alpha_i} \int_{t_1}^{t_2} f(u_j + \alpha_j \eta_j, u_j' + \alpha_j \eta_j') \, dt \right|_{\alpha_j = 0} = 0, \tag{7}$$

$$\int_{t_1}^{t_2} \left\{ \frac{\partial f(u_j, u_j')}{\partial u_i} \eta_i + \frac{\partial f(u_j, u_j')}{\partial u_i'} \eta_i' \right\} dt = 0.$$

Integrating by parts in the last relation and noting that the η_i are arbitrary and vanish at the endpoints of the interval of integration, we see that

$$\int_{t_1}^{t_2} \left\{ \frac{\partial f}{\partial u_i} \eta_i + \frac{d}{dt}\left(\frac{\partial f}{\partial u_i'} \eta_i\right) - \eta_i \frac{d}{dt}\left(\frac{\partial f}{\partial u_i'}\right) \right\} dt = 0,$$

(the middle term is struck out with an arrow marked "0")

$$\frac{\partial f}{\partial u_i} - \frac{d}{dt}\left(\frac{\partial f}{\partial u_i'}\right) = 0. \tag{8}$$

These are the Euler-Lagrange equations.

Mathematically this is equivalent to Hamilton's principle

$$\delta \int_{t_1}^{t_2} L\,dt = 0 \tag{9}$$

in the case where L is the Lagrangian characteristic of our dynamical system; and the Euler-Lagrange equations are just the equations of motion of our system.

2. Lagrangian Formalism for Continuous Systems and Fields

By analogy with the Lagrangian formalism of the dynamics of point particles, for a continuous system we consider the Lagrangian function as being an integral over the spatial volume of our system of some Lagrangian density $\mathcal{L}$ associated with the field:

$$L = \int_V \mathcal{L}\, d^3x. \tag{10}$$

Hamilton's principle now becomes:

$$\delta \int_{t_1}^{t_2} L\,dt = \delta \int_{t_1}^{t_2} \int_V \mathcal{L}\, d^3x\, dt = \delta \int_\tau \mathcal{L}\, d^4x = 0, \tag{11}$$

where the variations in the paths (of the dynamical variables) now vanish on the "surface" of τ, and x_1, x_2, x_3, x_0, are treated as independent variables. If one assumes a Lagrangian density of the form $\mathcal{L}(u_i(x), \partial_\mu u_i(x))$ and again requires that

$$\frac{\partial}{\partial a_i} I(a_j)\Big|_{a_j = 0} = 0, \tag{12}$$

then the Euler-Lagrange equations become

$$\frac{\partial \mathcal{L}}{\partial u_i} - \partial_\mu \left(\frac{\partial \mathcal{L}}{\partial(\partial_\mu u_i)} \right) = 0, \qquad \mu = 0 \ldots 3 . \tag{13}$$

(Throughout the discussion the tensor summation convention will be used.) This formalism seems to be the most general and concise way of formulating our physical laws and has many inherent advantages. The four-dimensional volume element d^4x is a Lorentz invariant, and our whole theory becomes Lorentz covariant if we also make the Lagrangian density a Lorentz-invariant scalar. The variables $u_i(x)$ must also have well-defined Lorentz transformations (i. e., they may transform like vectors, spinors, etc.).

3. Interacting Fields

Another advantage of the Lagrangian formalism is that it allows us to treat more than one field. This is usually done by writing the total Lagrangian as a sum of the "free-field" Lagrangians and their interactions:

$$\mathcal{L}_{total} = \mathcal{L}_A + \mathcal{L}_B + \mathcal{L}_{int} + \dots . \tag{14}$$

This is best illustrated by an example involving charged particles in an electromagnetic field. First we recall from classical dynamics that for a free particle Hamilton's principle assumes the form

$$\delta \int_{t_1}^{t_2} L \, dt = - \delta \int_{t_1}^{t_2} mc^2 \sqrt{1 - \beta^2} \, dt = 0, \tag{15}$$

which gives of course the equation of motion of a free particle:

$$\frac{d}{dt} \vec{p} = \frac{d}{dt} \left(\frac{m\vec{v}}{\sqrt{1 - \beta^2}} \right) = 0. \tag{16}$$

Next we note that we can define the electromagnetic field tensor $F_{\mu\nu}$ in terms of the four-vector potential $A_\mu(x)$,

$$F_{\mu\nu} = \partial_\nu A_\mu - \partial_\mu A_\nu , \tag{17}$$

and form a Lagrangian scalar density which gives the equations of the free electromagnetic field. In fact one sees that if we choose [3]

$$\mathcal{L}_{em} = -\tfrac{1}{4} F_{\mu\nu} F^{\mu\nu} \tag{18}$$

then Hamilton's principle

$$\delta \int \mathcal{L}_{em} \, d^4x = 0,$$

$$\delta \int -\tfrac{1}{4} (\partial_\nu A_\mu - \partial_\mu A_\nu)(\partial^\nu A^\mu - \partial^\mu A^\nu)\, d^4x = 0, \tag{19}$$

$$\delta \int -\tfrac{1}{2} \left[(\partial_\nu A_\mu)(\partial^\nu A^\mu) - (\partial_\nu A_\mu)(\partial^\mu A^\nu)\right] d^4x = 0$$

gives the Euler-Lagrange equations

$$\partial_\nu (\partial^\nu A^\mu - \partial^\mu A^\nu) = 0,$$

or (20)

$$\partial_\nu F^{\mu\nu} = 0 .$$

These are just the free-field Maxwell's equations

$$\vec{\nabla} \times \vec{H} - \frac{\partial \vec{E}}{\partial t} = 0,$$

$$\vec{\nabla} \cdot \vec{E} = 0, \tag{21}$$

where

$$\vec{E} = \vec{\nabla} A_0 - \frac{\partial}{\partial x^0} \vec{A},$$

$$\vec{H} = \vec{\nabla} \times \vec{A} . \tag{22}$$

Let us observe what form the interaction Lagrangian might take for the system consisting of both the charged particle and the electromagnetic field. It must contain a term characterizing the charged particle (in particular its charge e) and a term characterizing the field A_μ. For individual particles it is usually taken to be

$$\frac{e}{c} \int_a^b A_\mu \, dx^\mu ,$$

or equivalently (23)

$$\int_{t_1}^{t_2} \left(\frac{e}{c} \vec{A} \cdot \vec{v} - e\phi \right) dt.$$

Thus, for a system of particles interacting with the electromagnetic field the total Lagrangian would be:

$$L_{total} = -\Sigma mc^2 \sqrt{1-\beta^2} + \Sigma\left(\frac{e}{c}\vec{A}\cdot\vec{v} - e\phi\right)$$
$$-\tfrac{1}{4}\int F_{\mu\nu}F^{\mu\nu}\, d^3x. \qquad (24)$$

Applying Hamilton's principle to this total Lagrangian and varying the particle variables (the particle trajectories) and the field variables A_μ would yield equations giving us the behavior of the field due to particle motion and the motion of the particles due to the field. However, we take a less ambitious approach and first assume that only one particle is present, and that the field is given and is not affected by the motion of the particle. Then the variation with respect to the particle parameter $\vec{r}$ will give the equations of motion of a particle in the field,

$$\frac{\partial L}{\partial \vec{r}} = \frac{e}{c}\vec{\nabla}(\vec{A}\cdot\vec{v}) - e\vec{\nabla}\phi,$$
$$\frac{d}{dt}\left(\frac{\partial \mathcal{L}}{\partial \vec{v}}\right) = \frac{d}{dt}\left(\vec{p} + \frac{e}{c}\vec{A}\right), \qquad (25)$$

while the variation of the free-field Lagrangian is zero. By using a vector identity

$$\vec{\nabla}(\vec{C}\cdot\vec{D}) = (\vec{C}\cdot\vec{\nabla})\vec{D} + (\vec{D}\cdot\vec{\nabla})\vec{C} + \vec{C}\times(\vec{\nabla}\times\vec{D})$$
$$+ \vec{D}\times(\vec{\nabla}\times\vec{C}) \qquad (26)$$

we can transform our Euler-Lagrange equations to the form

$$\frac{d}{dt}\left(\vec{p} + \frac{e}{c}\vec{A}\right) = \frac{e}{c}(\vec{v}\cdot\vec{\nabla})\vec{A} + \frac{e}{c}\vec{v}\times(\vec{\nabla}\times\vec{A}) - e\vec{\nabla}\phi. \qquad (27)$$

Now

$$\frac{d\vec{A}}{dt} = \frac{\partial\vec{A}}{\partial t} + (\vec{v}\cdot\vec{\nabla})\vec{A}; \qquad (28)$$

so

$$\frac{d\vec{p}}{dt} = -\frac{e}{c} \frac{\partial \vec{A}}{\partial t} - e \vec{\nabla} \phi + \frac{e}{c} \vec{v} \times (\vec{\nabla} \times \vec{A})$$

$$= e(\vec{E} + \frac{\vec{v}}{c} \times \vec{H}),$$

(29)

which is just the Lorentz force equation.

Next, to find the equations of motion of the field itself in the presence of charges, we assume the motion of the charges to be given and vary only the field. For this case, it is convenient to consider a continuously distributed charge density ρ giving rise to our interaction term instead of a collection of point charges. Thus:

$$\int L_{int} \, dt = \Sigma \int_a^b \frac{e}{c} A_\mu \, dx^\mu$$

$$\rightarrow \int_a^b \int_V \frac{\rho}{c} A_\mu \, dx^\mu \, dV$$

$$= \int_\tau \frac{\rho}{c} \frac{dx^\mu}{dt} A_\mu \, dV \, dt$$

$$= \int_\tau J^\mu A_\mu \, d^4x.$$

(30)

The contribution from this term will be

$$\frac{\partial \mathscr{L}_{int}}{\partial A_\mu} = J^\mu ,$$

(31)

and we have already found that the contribution from the field only was

$$\partial_\nu F^{\mu\nu} .$$

(32)

So now the Euler-Lagrange equations giving the equations of the electromagnetic field in the presence of sources are

$$\partial_\nu F^{\mu\nu} - J^\mu = 0.$$

(33)

These are, of course, just the Maxwell equations

$$\vec{\nabla} \times \vec{H} - \frac{\partial \vec{E}}{\partial t} = \vec{J},$$
$$\vec{\nabla} \cdot \vec{E} = \rho . \tag{34}$$

4. Conservation Laws - Noether's Theorem

Consider the variation of the Lagrangian density

$$\delta \int_T \mathcal{L}(u^i, \partial_\mu u^i)\, d^4x = 0. \tag{35}$$

Noether showed[4] that for every transformation of the variables

$$u^i(x) \rightarrow u^i(x) + \psi^i(x, \eta^j), \; \psi^i(x, 0) = 0 \tag{36}$$

which depends on s real parameters η^j and which leaves the Lagrangian invariant, there corresponds a conservation law of the form

$$\partial_\mu \left[\sum_i \frac{\partial \mathcal{L}}{\partial(\partial_\mu u^i)} \psi^i_j(x) \right] = 0, \qquad j = 1 \ldots s,$$

where

$$\psi^i_j(x) = \left. \frac{\partial \psi^i(x, \eta)}{\partial \eta_j} \right|_{\eta = 0} . \tag{37}$$

There is also a second part to the theorem which has to do with our requirement that $\mathcal{L}$ be a Lorentz invariant - more specifically, that $\mathcal{L}$ be invariant under the group of inhomogeneous proper orthochronous Lorentz (I. P. O. L.) transformations. These are the Lorentz transformations

$$x'^\mu = a^\mu{}_\nu x^\nu + b^\mu \tag{38}$$

satisfying the requirements

$$\text{Det } a^\mu{}_\nu = 1,$$
$$a^0{}_0 \geqq 1. \tag{39}$$

The transformation properties of the $u^i(x)$ for these transformations are given by

$$u'^i(x') \equiv u'^i(a^\mu{}_\nu x^\nu + b^\mu) = \sum_j S^i_j u^j(x), \tag{40}$$

where the S^i_j are determined only by $a^\mu{}_\nu$ and not b^μ. (That is, the $u^i(x)$ transform according to a representation of the homogeneous proper orthochronous Lorentz (P. O. L.) group.) The second part of Noether's theorem states that when we require that $\mathcal{L}$ be invariant under

$$\begin{aligned} x^\mu &\to x'^\mu = a^\mu{}_\nu x^\nu + b^\mu, \\ u^i(x) &\to u'^i(x') = \sum_j S^i_j u^j(x), \end{aligned} \tag{41}$$

we arrive at a conservation law

$$\begin{aligned} \partial_\mu \Bigg\{ &- \sum_i \frac{\partial \mathcal{L}}{\partial(\partial_\mu u^i)} \partial_\tau u^i \left[\frac{\partial a^\tau{}_\lambda}{\partial \eta^k} x^\lambda + \frac{\partial b^\tau}{\partial \eta^k}\right]_{\eta=0} \\ &+ \sum_{i,j} \frac{\partial \mathcal{L}}{\partial(\partial_\mu u^i)} \left[\frac{\partial S^i_j}{\partial \eta^k}\right]_{\eta=0} u^j + \mathcal{L}\left[\frac{\partial a^\mu{}_\lambda}{\partial \eta^k} x^\lambda + \frac{\partial b^\mu}{\partial \eta^k}\right]_{\eta=0} \Bigg\} = 0. \end{aligned} \tag{42}$$

This will turn out to be the expression giving the conservation of energy and linear and angular momentum, and it is purely a result of invariance of $\mathcal{L}$ under I. P. O. L. transformations.

The $\eta^1 \ldots \eta^{10}$ are in this case ten parameters used to express $a^\mu{}_\nu$, b^μ in such a way that as the η^k vary the $a^\mu{}_\nu$, b^μ vary over all I. P. O. L. transformations; this can be done because the I. P. O. L. group is a ten-parameter group. For the case of a pure translation, one has

$$a^\mu{}_\nu = 0,$$

$$\eta^0, \eta^1, \eta^2, \eta^3 \longleftrightarrow b^0, b^1, b^2, b^3, \tag{43}$$

and

$$\frac{\partial b^\mu}{\partial \eta^\nu} = \delta^\mu_\nu .$$

Using this and remembering that S^i_j is a function of $a^\mu{}_\nu$ only, we find that

$$\partial_\mu\left(\sum_i \frac{\partial \mathcal{L}}{\partial(\partial_\mu u^i)} \partial^\nu u^i - g^{\mu\nu}\mathcal{L}\right) = 0. \tag{44}$$

We define the quantity in parentheses as $T^{\nu\mu}$, so

$$\partial_\mu T^{\nu\mu} = 0. \tag{45}$$

$T^{\nu\mu}$ is thus identified as the stress-energy tensor density from which the total four-momentum of the system may be obtained:

$$P^\nu = \int_{\substack{\text{all}\\ \text{space}}} T^{\nu 0}\, dV = \text{constant}. \tag{46}$$

P^0 is identified as the energy of the system.

Similarly, if we consider only "rotations"

$$a^\mu{}_\nu = I + \begin{pmatrix} 0 & \omega^0{}_1 & \omega^0{}_2 & \omega^0{}_3 \\ \omega^1{}_0 & 0 & \omega^1{}_2 & \omega^1{}_3 \\ \omega^2{}_0 & \omega^2{}_1 & 0 & \omega^2{}_3 \\ \omega^3{}_0 & \omega^3{}_1 & \omega^3{}_2 & 0 \end{pmatrix} + 0(\omega^2) \tag{47}$$

we can take $\eta^k = \omega^\mu{}_\nu$, $\nu > \mu$ (above diagonal).

So

$$\left.\frac{\partial a^\mu{}_\nu}{\partial \eta^k}\right|_{\eta=0} = \left.\frac{\partial a^\mu{}_\nu}{\partial \omega^\lambda{}_\tau}\right|_{\omega=0} = \delta^\mu_\lambda\, \delta^\tau_\nu - g^{\mu\tau} g_{\lambda\nu}, \tag{48}$$

giving

$$\partial_\mu\left\{x^\xi T^{\eta\mu} - x^\eta T^{\xi\mu} - g^{\eta\lambda} \sum_{i,j} \frac{\partial \mathcal{L}}{\partial(\partial_\mu u^i)} \left[\frac{\partial S^i_j}{\partial \omega^\lambda{}_\xi}\right]_{\omega=0} u^j\right\} = 0, \tag{49}$$

or

$$\partial_\mu m^{\eta\xi\mu} = 0, \qquad \int_{\substack{\text{all}\\ \text{space}}} m^{\eta\xi 0}\, dV = \text{constant}. \tag{50}$$

Thus we have obtained statements of the conservation of energy and of the linear and angular momentum of the system as a result of the invariance of $\mathcal{L}$ under I. P. O. L. transformations.

Section II. EXPERIMENTAL EVIDENCE FOR GRAVITATIONAL THEORIES

1. Introduction

The best known and most widely accepted theory of gravitation (Einstein's General Theory of Relativity), though it is probably the most elegant of our physical theories, has but a few initial experimental observations to rely on. We will mention the observational data that are available, and from these draw some implications about our theory.

The experiments to be discussed fall into two classes:

1) "null" experiments;

2) "positive results" experiments.

By the first class, we mean that a failure to detect certain effects might give us fundamental starting points on which to build our theory. We shall begin by discussing the "null" experiments.

The most famous of these, the Eötvos experiment (1890), showed by using a torsion balance to compare the inertial (centripetal) forces arising from the Earth's rotation with the gravitational forces due to the Earth's mass that to one part in 10^9 the gravitational and inertial masses are equivalent. Dicke and Roll have recently (1963) repeated Eötvos' experiment with the same result to one part in 10^{11}.

Another "null" result which sheds light on the isotropy of space has been performed at Yale and Denver. It considers a Li^7 nucleus which when placed in a magnetic field has its ground state split into four levels.

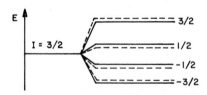

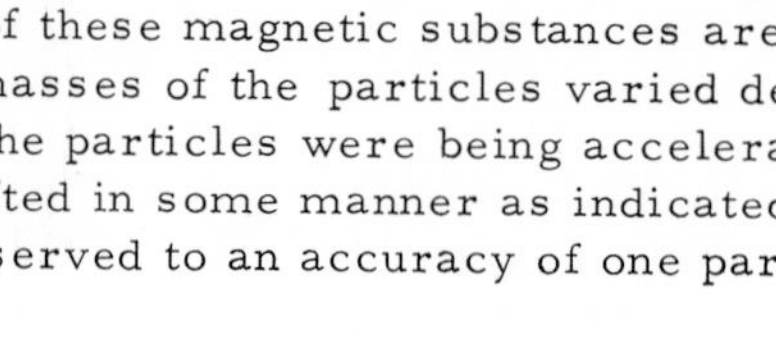

The energy levels of these magnetic substances are very sensitive, and if the inertial masses of the particles varied depending on the direction in which the particles were being accelerated then the energy levels would be shifted in some manner as indicated by the dotted lines. But this was not observed to an accuracy of one part in 10^{23} using nuclear magnetic resonance. The implication of this isotropy of space is that it excludes more than one tensor field from the total effect known as gravitation.[5]

Now let us mention the three experiments which give positive results for the general theory of relativity (G. T. R.) in particular.

Recently (1963) the Mössbauer effect has been used to measure the gravitational red shift, and the result obtained agrees to a high degree of accuracy with the shift in frequency of spectral lines predicted by G. T. R. Using a Co^{57} source and a Fe^{57} absorber, a shift was measured at Harvard to an accuracy of five parts in 10^{15}, using a potential difference corresponding to a change in height of 74 feet. (The predictions for the gravitational red shift follow elegantly and in a straightforward manner from G. T. R., but it should be mentioned that the same results can be obtained using Newtonian gravitation and considering the equivalence of mass and energy

$$E = mc^2 = h\nu\,.) \tag{51}$$

Deflection of a light ray by the gravitational field of the sun as the ray passes through the sun's vicinity is another test. This phenomenon is best measured during eclipses. The predicted value is

$$\theta = \frac{4GM}{c^2 r_0} \approx 1.75 \text{ sec}; \tag{52}$$

and it agrees to within 10 percent with the measured value, which has a probable error of 10 percent.

Probably the most significant experiment in agreement with G.T.R. is the one involving the precession of the perihelion of Mercury. This is because it involves all of the components of the gravitational field (thus verifying the tensor nature of the gravitational field), and because its value (six times that predicted by special relativity) agrees within 1 percent with G. T. R. The figures are

Measured precession: $43.11 \pm .45$ seconds of arc per century;

Precession predicted by G.T.R.: 43.03 seconds of arc per century.

However, there is a possibility of a perturbing influence due to the oblateness of the sun and its mass distribution. This would increase the precession rate, and would indicate that the gravitational field is probably a combination of a tensor field and a scalar field. For this reason, there is an experiment presently underway at Princeton to measure the oblateness of the sun.

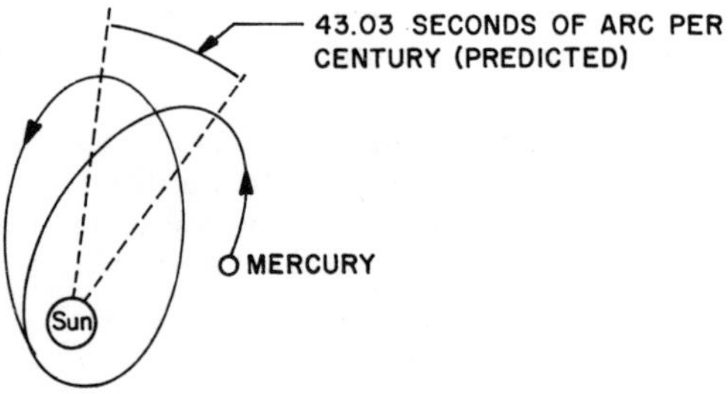

NOTE: Most of this is excellently discussed by R. H. Dicke, P. C. Roll, and J. Weber in "Gravity Experiments," International Science and Technology, May 1964.

2. A "Gedanken" Experiment

A. Schield, in an idealized "Gedanken" experiment,[5] has indicated that the special theory of relativity and the existence of a gravitational red shift do not form a consistent theoretical system. This may be seen as follows. Consider a spherically-symmetric gravitating body of mass M at rest in an empty space. We assume that special relativity holds and space-time is "flat":

$$ds^2 = dt^2 - dx_1^2 - dx_2^2 - dx_3^2, \tag{53}$$

where ds is the element of proper time measured by a physical clock along its world line. The mass M is assumed at rest in an inertial frame x_μ; therefore, the world line of any particle at rest near the surface of M will be a straight line parallel to the t axis. Assume the particle to be an atomic clock at A, and assume another clock at a higher potential at B. In the figure below, AA' is the world line of clock A and BB' that of clock B. Now AB is the world line of the light signal used to compare the readings of the two clocks at the beginning of the experiment and A'B' the world line of the signal used at its end. Since this is a static gravitational field, the propagation properties of light are the same from A to B as from A' to B'; and thus AB and A'B' will be parallel. This in turn implies BB' and AA' or $S_V + \Delta V$ and S_V are equal if we have drawn our diagram in a "flat",

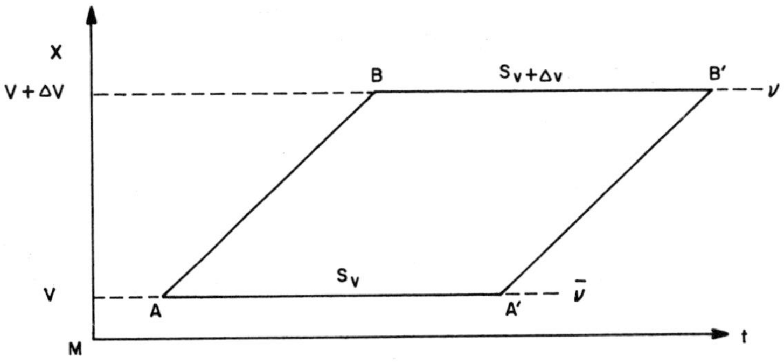

not curved, geometry. However, for a change in potential ΔV the formula for the gravitational red shift is:

$$\Delta V = \frac{\bar{\nu} - \nu}{\nu} . \tag{54}$$

This is related to the time by $\nu = n/s$, giving $(s - \bar{s})/\bar{s} = \Delta V$. The last equation states that BB' is not equal to AA', and AB and A'B' are not parallel. Schield draws the conclusion that a geometry in the absence of parallelism is characteristic of curved space, or that a curved geometry of space-time is implied by the above experiment.

Section III. THE EQUIVALENCE PRINCIPLE, GENERAL COVARIANCE, AND PRELIMINARIES

1. The Equivalence Principle

The experimental equivalence of the gravitational and inertial masses, which was mentioned in the previous section, was given the role of a theoretical foundation by Einstein in his equivalence principle. He pointed out that the equivalence of the two kinds of masses may be understood in terms of the equivalence of a rest (inertial) frame in a uniform gravitational field and an accelerated frame in a gravitational-field-free region.

2. General Covariance

Since by local measurement we cannot distinguish between an inertial frame and a freely falling system in a gravitational field, Einstein postulated that all systems of coordinates (not only inertial ones) are equally good for the description of the laws of physics; and these laws should have the same form in all systems of coordinates.

3. The Metric Tensor

In four-space the set of transformations which maintain the invariance of

$$ds^2 = (dx^0)^2 - (dx^1)^2 - (dx^2)^2 - (dx^3)^2 \tag{55}$$

defines what we call the homogeneous Lorentz group. The matrices which form a representation of this group in four-space are just the Lorentz transformation matrices. It will prove to be convenient to write our ds^2 in the form

$$ds^2 = g_{\mu\nu}\, dx^\mu\, dx^\nu\,, \tag{56}$$

where

$$g_{\mu\nu} = \begin{pmatrix} 1 & 0 & 0 & 0 \\ 0 & -1 & 0 & 0 \\ 0 & 0 & -1 & 0 \\ 0 & 0 & 0 & -1 \end{pmatrix}$$

is called the metric tensor. Whenever we have a length defined in our space, the space is called a metric space; and the metric tensor is a convenient way of specifying the properties of that space. For example, a curved two-dimensional space on the surface of a sphere is described by the squared infinitesimal line element

$$ds^2 = r^2 d\theta^2 + r^2 \sin^2\theta \, d\varphi^2 ,$$

so that

$$g_{\mu\nu} = \begin{pmatrix} r^2 & 0 \\ 0 & r^2 \sin^2 \theta \end{pmatrix} . \tag{57}$$

A space with a completely general metric

$$g_{\mu\nu}(x) = \begin{pmatrix} g_{00}(x) & g_{01}(x) & g_{02}(x) & g_{03}(x) \\ g_{10}(x) & g_{11}(x) & g_{12}(x) & g_{13}(x) \\ g_{20}(x) & g_{21}(x) & g_{22}(x) & g_{23}(x) \\ g_{30}(x) & g_{31}(x) & g_{32}(x) & g_{33}(x) \end{pmatrix} \tag{58}$$

defining a squared infinitesimal distance ds^2 which is an invariant homogeneous quadratic function of the coordinate differentials

$$ds^2 = g_{\mu\nu} \, dx^\mu \, dx^\nu \tag{59}$$

is called a Riemannian space.

It is convenient to also define a set of quantities $g^{\mu\kappa}$ by the equations

$$g_{\mu\nu} \, g^{\mu\kappa} = \delta^\kappa_\nu . \tag{60}$$

If we introduce the concepts of covariant and contravariant vectors which have the respective transformation laws

$$A'_\alpha = \frac{\partial x^\beta}{\partial x'^\alpha} A_\beta , \quad A'^\alpha = \frac{\partial x'^\alpha}{\partial x^\beta} A^\beta , \tag{61}$$

then these $g_{\mu\nu}$ and $g^{\mu\nu}$ allow us to pass from the covariant form of a vector to its contravariant form, and vice versa:

$$A^\alpha = g^{\alpha\beta} A_\beta , \text{ etc.} \tag{62}$$

Higher order tensors are defined as quantities which transform like products of two or more vectors. This tensor calculus in Riemannian spaces turns out to be very convenient as a means of formulating Einstein's general covariance principle.

4. Parallel Displacement and Covariant Differentiation

For an arbitrary coordinate system, the infinitesimal parallel displacement of a vector A_μ from a point P to point P' is defined as that operation which leaves $A_\mu B^\mu$ invariant (B^μ being an arbitrary vector). Now in curvilinear coordinates, the components of A_μ would be expected to change under a parallel displacement. If δA_μ is this change, it should be a linear function of the coordinate differentials and of the vector components A^ν:

$$\delta A^\nu = -\Gamma^\nu_{\alpha\beta} A^\alpha dx^\beta , \tag{63}$$

where

$$\Gamma^\nu_{\alpha\beta} = \Gamma^\nu_{\beta\alpha} .$$

We can also introduce our Riemannian metric and write the $\Gamma^\nu_{\alpha\beta}$ in terms of this metric as follows:

$$\begin{aligned} 0 &= \delta(A_\mu A^\mu) \\ &= g_{\mu\nu}(P')(A^\nu + \delta A^\nu)(A^\mu + \delta A^\mu) - g_{\mu\nu}(P) A^\mu A^\nu , \end{aligned} \tag{64}$$

which gives

$$\frac{\partial g_{\mu\alpha}}{\partial x^\nu} - g_{\mu\beta}\Gamma^\beta_{\alpha\nu} - g_{\alpha\beta}\Gamma^\beta_{\mu\nu} = 0. \tag{65}$$

By carrying out cyclic permutations of the indices and adding, we find that

$$\Gamma^\nu_{\mu\alpha} = \tfrac{1}{2} g^{\nu\kappa}\left(\frac{\partial g_{\kappa\mu}}{\partial x^\alpha} + \frac{\partial g_{\kappa\alpha}}{\partial x^\mu} - \frac{\partial g_{\mu\alpha}}{\partial x^\kappa}\right). \tag{66}$$

The quantities $\Gamma^\nu_{\mu\alpha}$ are called the "affine connection."

Now an ordinary partial derivative of a vector will not be a tensor, and we want to define a derivative which will be. Consider a vector A^μ at P; at a neighboring point the vector is

$$A^\mu + dA^\mu , \tag{67}$$

while the vector resulting from a parallel displacement to that point will be

$$A^{\mu} + \delta A^{\mu}. \tag{68}$$

Subtracting one expression from the other will give us a vector, because the difference of two vectors at the same point will still be a vector:

$$dA^{\mu} - \delta A^{\mu} = \left(\frac{\partial A^{\mu}}{\partial x^{\sigma}} + \Gamma^{\mu}_{\alpha\sigma} A^{\alpha} \right) dx^{\sigma}. \tag{69}$$

The quantity

$$\frac{\partial A^{\mu}}{\partial x^{\sigma}} + \Gamma^{\mu}_{\alpha\sigma} A^{\alpha} \tag{70}$$

is defined as the "covariant derivative" of A^{μ}, and this covariant derivative is denoted by $A^{\mu}{}_{;\sigma}$. That is,

$$A^{\mu}{}_{;\sigma} = \frac{\partial A^{\mu}}{\partial x^{\sigma}} + \Gamma^{\mu}_{\alpha\sigma} A^{\alpha}. \tag{71}$$

Similarly one finds the covariant derivative of A_{μ} to be

$$A_{\mu;\sigma} = \frac{\partial A_{\mu}}{\partial x^{\sigma}} - \Gamma^{\alpha}_{\mu\sigma} A_{\alpha}. \tag{72}$$

5. The Riemann Curvature Tensor

If we move a vector by parallel displacement around a closed curve and get the same vector, then the affine connection is said to be integrable. This property is invariant under various choices of coordinates, and is a property of the space. It can be shown that whenever the parallel displacement defined by $\Gamma^{\alpha}_{\mu\nu}$ is integrable, then the space is flat, i.e., the $g_{\mu\nu}$'s are constants. The necessary and sufficient conditions for integrability are:

$$\begin{aligned} &\Gamma^{\eta}_{\lambda\nu,\kappa} - \Gamma^{\eta}_{\lambda\kappa,\nu} + \Gamma^{\eta}_{\sigma\kappa} \Gamma^{\sigma}_{\lambda\nu} - \Gamma^{\eta}_{\sigma\nu} \Gamma^{\sigma}_{\lambda\kappa} \\ &\equiv R_{\nu\kappa\lambda}{}^{\eta} = 0. \end{aligned} \tag{73}$$

It may also be shown that

$$A^{\eta}{}_{;\nu;\kappa} - A^{\eta}{}_{;\kappa;\nu} = R_{\nu\kappa\lambda}{}^{\eta} A^{\lambda}. \tag{74}$$

This last result shows that $R_{\nu\kappa\lambda}{}^{\eta}$ is a tensor, and we shall call it the Riemann curvature tensor. The $R_{\nu\kappa\lambda}{}^{\eta}$ can be defined with any affine connection, but it has certain symmetry properties which are associated with a metric. It is antisymmetric in ν and κ, and if $\Gamma^{\nu}_{\mu\kappa}$ is symmetric we can also show that

$$R_{\nu\kappa\lambda}{}^{\eta} + R_{\kappa\lambda\nu}{}^{\eta} + R_{\lambda\nu\kappa}{}^{\eta} = 0. \tag{75}$$

From this last relation one obtains the important differential identities called the Bianchi identities[6]

$$R_{\nu\kappa\sigma}{}^{\eta}{}_{;\lambda} + R_{\kappa\lambda\sigma}{}^{\eta}{}_{;\nu} + R_{\lambda\nu\sigma}{}^{\eta}{}_{;\kappa} = 0. \tag{76}$$

Section IV. GRAVITATIONAL FIELD EQUATIONS

1. Free Field Equations

The equivalence principle, which equates regions of nonzero gravitational field with noninertial coordinate systems, leads us to a gravitational-field Lagrangian density $\mathcal{L}_g$ determined purely from the geometrical properties of space. For the purpose of constructing $\mathcal{L}_g$, we have the metric tensor $g_{\mu\nu}$ and the affine connections $\Gamma^{\nu}_{\kappa\lambda}$; but it is impossible to construct nontrivial invariants from only $g_{\mu\nu}$ and $\Gamma^{\nu}_{\kappa\lambda}$, since we may define coordinate systems where the $\Gamma^{\nu}_{\kappa\lambda}$ vanish at a point. We thus find out that the simplest nontrivial invariant which can be formed which characterizes the property of our space-time manifold is the quantity obtained by contracting the curvature tensor

$$R_{\nu\kappa\lambda}{}^{\eta} \equiv \Gamma^{\eta}_{\lambda\nu,\kappa} - \Gamma^{\eta}_{\lambda\kappa,\nu} + \Gamma^{\eta}_{\sigma\kappa}\Gamma^{\sigma}_{\lambda\nu} - \Gamma^{\eta}_{\sigma\nu}\Gamma^{\sigma}_{\lambda\kappa} \tag{77}$$

This contracted tensor is

$$R \equiv g^{\kappa\lambda} R_{\kappa\lambda} \equiv g^{\kappa\lambda} R_{\nu\kappa\lambda}{}^{\nu}. \tag{78}$$

We can then write the invariant expression

$$S_g = \int_T \mathcal{L}_g \sqrt{-g}\, d^4x = \int_T R\sqrt{-g}\, d^4x \tag{79}$$

for the action. Here $\sqrt{-g}$ is the Jacobian of the transformation, and is needed to make $(\sqrt{-g}\, d^4x)$ a general-relativistic invariant. Therefore, our gravitational free-field equations will be given by

$$\delta S_g = \delta \int_T R\sqrt{-g}\, d^4x = 0. \tag{80}$$

At this point it is interesting to note that if in $\mathcal{L}_g$ we consider the $\Gamma^{\mu}_{\lambda\kappa}$ as the independent variables and the $g_{\mu\nu}$ as constant, then the equations of motion will lead to the requirement

$$\Gamma^{\nu}_{\kappa\lambda} = \tfrac{1}{2} g^{\nu\eta}\left(\frac{\partial g_{\eta\kappa}}{\partial x^{\lambda}} + \frac{\partial g_{\eta\lambda}}{\partial x^{\kappa}} - \frac{\partial g_{\kappa\lambda}}{\partial x^{\eta}}\right). \tag{81}$$

This, as we saw before, is just the relation of $\Gamma^{\mu}_{\kappa\lambda}$ to the metric tensor $g_{\mu\nu}$. Thus, it is equivalent to write $\mathscr{L}_g$ in terms of $g_{\mu\nu}$ and consider them as the variables (potentials) of the gravitational field.[3] The variational principle

$$\delta \int_{\tau} \mathscr{L}_g \sqrt{-g} \; d^4x = 0 \tag{82}$$

then gives

$$\frac{\partial}{\partial g^{\mu\nu}} \left(\mathscr{L}_g \sqrt{-g} \right) - \partial_{\kappa} \left[\frac{\partial}{\partial (g^{\mu\nu},_{\kappa})} \left(\mathscr{L}_g \sqrt{-g} \right) \right] = 0. \tag{83}$$

It will be noticed that $\mathscr{L}_g$ contains derivatives of $g_{\mu\nu}$ of higher than first order. This presents no problem in considering the g's as independent variables, however, because the terms containing second derivatives of $g_{\mu\nu}$ can be separated and made to vanish. In fact,

$$\sqrt{-g} \; R = \sqrt{-g} \; g^{\mu\nu} R_{\mu\nu}$$

$$= \sqrt{-g} \left[g^{\mu\nu} \Gamma^{\lambda}_{\mu\nu},_{\lambda} - g^{\mu\nu} \Gamma^{\lambda}_{\mu\lambda},_{\nu} + g^{\mu\nu} \Gamma^{\lambda}_{\mu\nu} \Gamma^{\eta}_{\lambda\eta} - g^{\mu\nu} \Gamma^{\eta}_{\mu\lambda} \Gamma^{\lambda}_{\nu\eta} \right], \tag{84}$$

and since

$$\frac{\partial}{\partial x^{\lambda}} \left(\sqrt{-g} \; g^{\mu\nu} \Gamma^{\lambda}_{\mu\nu} \right) = \sqrt{-g} \; g^{\mu\nu} \Gamma^{\lambda}_{\mu\nu},_{\lambda} + \Gamma^{\lambda}_{\mu\nu} \frac{\partial}{\partial x^{\lambda}} \left(\sqrt{-g} \; g^{\mu\nu} \right),$$

$$\frac{\partial}{\partial x^{\nu}} \left(\sqrt{-g} \; g^{\mu\nu} \Gamma^{\lambda}_{\mu\lambda} \right) = \sqrt{-g} \; g^{\mu\nu} \Gamma^{\lambda}_{\mu\lambda},_{\nu} + \Gamma^{\lambda}_{\mu\lambda} \frac{\partial}{\partial x^{\nu}} \left(\sqrt{-g} \; g^{\mu\nu} \right), \tag{85}$$

the first two terms in Equation (84) are total derivatives. Using Gauss' theorem

$$\int_{S_{\tau}} A_{\mu} \; dS^{\mu} = \int_{\tau} \frac{\partial A_{\mu}}{\partial x_{\mu}} \; d^4x \tag{86}$$

and the fact that the variation $\delta \mathscr{L}_g$ vanishes on the surface S_{τ} shows that these terms can be dropped. Thus, we need consider only

$$\sqrt{-g} \; G \equiv \Gamma^{\eta}_{\mu\eta} \frac{\partial}{\partial x^{\nu}} \left(\sqrt{-g} \; g^{\mu\nu} \right) - \Gamma^{\lambda}_{\mu\nu} \frac{\partial}{\partial x^{\lambda}} \left(\sqrt{-g} \; g^{\mu\nu} \right)$$

$$- \left(\Gamma^{\eta}_{\mu\lambda} \Gamma^{\lambda}_{\nu\eta} - \Gamma^{\lambda}_{\mu\nu} \Gamma^{\eta}_{\lambda\eta} \right) g^{\mu\nu} \sqrt{-g} \; . \tag{87}$$

124

Using the identity[3]

$$g^{\kappa\lambda}\,\Gamma^{\nu}_{\kappa\lambda} = -\frac{1}{\sqrt{-g}}\,\frac{\partial}{\partial x^{\kappa}}\left(\sqrt{-g}\;g^{\nu\kappa}\right), \tag{88}$$

we get

$$\sqrt{-g}\,G = \mathcal{L}_g\sqrt{-g} = \sqrt{-g}\;g^{\mu\nu}\left(\Gamma^{\eta}_{\mu\lambda}\,\Gamma^{\lambda}_{\kappa\eta} - \Gamma^{\lambda}_{\mu\nu}\,\Gamma^{\eta}_{\lambda\eta}\right), \tag{89}$$

from which the equations of motion for the free gravitational field are of course found to be

$$\frac{\partial}{\partial g^{\mu\nu}}\left(G\sqrt{-g}\right) - \partial_{\lambda}\left[\frac{\partial}{\partial g^{\mu\nu}{}_{,\lambda}}\left(G\sqrt{-g}\right)\right] = 0\,. \tag{90}$$

After performing these operations and (with some effort) simplifying the resulting expressions, we can put the Euler-Lagrange equations above in the form:

$$(R_{\mu\nu} - \tfrac{1}{2}g_{\mu\nu}R)\sqrt{-g} = 0 \equiv G_{\mu\nu}\sqrt{-g}\,. \tag{91}$$

NOTE: This does not imply that space-time is "flat" in vacuum; for that we need $R_{\kappa\lambda\eta}{}^{\nu} = 0$.

Later we will see that the existence of the Bianchi identities implies a conservation law for $G_{\mu\nu}$.

2. Field Equations with Other Fields Present

Following our Lagrangian formalism of field theory we can write

$$\mathcal{L}_{total} = \mathcal{L}_g + \mathcal{L}_F \tag{92}$$

when more than one field is present, where here $\mathcal{L}_F$ will be the Lagrangian density due to all other fields. In this case, however, we do not have an explicit interaction term $\mathcal{L}_I$ as in classical (and quantum-mechanical) Lagrangian formulations; the gravitational field is a very special field, and its interaction is already contained implicitly because it governs the underlying space-time metric for all fields. In other words, there are no "free field" equations; all of our physical fields have an associated metric tensor $g_{\mu\nu}$ underlying them and thus an associated gravitational field. This will be made clearer by the following examples.

Assume that the fields giving rise to $\mathcal{L}_F$ are given and we want to know what the equations governing the gravitational field are. We then vary our total action with respect to the variables $g_{\mu\nu}$, getting

$$\frac{\partial \mathcal{L}}{\partial g_{\mu\nu}} - \frac{\partial}{\partial x^\lambda} \frac{\partial \mathcal{L}}{\partial g_{\mu\nu,\lambda}} = 0, \tag{93}$$

or

$$\sqrt{-g}\, G_{\mu\nu} + \alpha\left[\frac{\partial}{\partial g_{\mu\nu}}\left(\mathcal{L}_F \sqrt{-g}\right) - \frac{\partial}{\partial x^\lambda} \frac{\partial}{\partial g_{\mu\nu,\lambda}}\left(\mathcal{L}_F \sqrt{-g}\right)\right] = 0 \tag{94}$$

(where α is a constant determining the coupling between the gravitational and other fields). At this point, we digress a second to notice that the Bianchi identities introduced earlier, when contracted, state the conservation of $G_{\mu\nu}$:

$$R_{\nu\kappa\sigma}{}^\eta{}_{;\mu} + R_{\kappa\mu\sigma}{}^\eta{}_{;\nu} + R_{\mu\nu\sigma}{}^\eta{}_{;\kappa} = 0. \tag{95}$$

Contracting ν and η, and κ and σ and using the symmetry properties of $R_{\mu\nu\kappa}{}^\eta$ we get[6]

$$(R^{\mu\nu} - \tfrac{1}{2} g^{\mu\nu} R)_{;\nu} = 0 = G^{\mu\nu}{}_{;\nu}. \tag{96}$$

Since the generalized statement of the conservation of the stress-energy tensor is

$$T^{\mu\nu}{}_{;\nu} = 0, \tag{97}$$

this suggests that in Equation (94) we define

$$-\left[\frac{\partial}{\partial g_{\mu\nu}}\left(\mathcal{L}_F \sqrt{-g}\right) - \frac{\partial}{\partial x^\lambda} \frac{\partial}{\partial g_{\mu\nu,\lambda}}\left(\mathcal{L}_F \sqrt{-g}\right)\right] \equiv \tfrac{1}{2}\sqrt{-g}\, T^{\mu\nu}, \tag{98}$$

since it will have to be a conserved quantity. Then our gravitational field equations become

$$G^{\mu\nu} - \alpha\, T^{\mu\nu} = 0,$$

126

satisfying (99)

$$(G^{\mu\nu} - \alpha T^{\mu\nu})_{;\nu} = -\alpha T^{\mu\nu}{}_{;\nu} \equiv 0.$$

The above definition of the stress-energy tensor has the advantage that it is always symmetric.

We can also show that $T^{\mu\nu}$ is explicitly conserved when $\mathcal{L}_F$ is invariant under infinitesimal translations of the origin, i. e.,

$$x^{\mu} \rightarrow x'^{\mu} = x^{\mu} + \xi^{\mu} \tag{100}$$

(just as in Noether's theorem for the special relativistic case). Under small displacements ξ^{μ} the change in $g^{\mu\nu}(x)$ can be written

$$\delta g^{\mu\nu} = g'^{\mu\nu}(x) - g^{\mu\nu}(x) = \xi^{\mu;\nu} + \xi^{\nu;\mu}. \tag{101}$$

Going back to our variational principle

$$\delta S_F = \delta \int_T \mathcal{L}_F \sqrt{-g}\, d^4x = -\tfrac{1}{2} \int_T T_{\mu\nu}\, \delta g^{\mu\nu} \sqrt{-g}\, d^4x \tag{102}$$

and assuming that the variation in $\delta g^{\mu\nu}$ is due to the transformation in Equation (101), and using the fact that $T_{\mu\nu}$ is symmetric, we see that

$$\begin{aligned} 0 = -\delta S_F &= \int_T T_{\mu\nu}\, \xi^{\mu;\nu} \sqrt{-g}\, d^4x \\ &= \int_T \left[\left(T_{\mu\nu}\, \xi^{\mu} \right)^{;\nu} \sqrt{-g} - T_{\mu\nu}{}^{;\nu}\, \xi^{\mu} \sqrt{-g} \right] d^4x . \end{aligned} \tag{103}$$

Since

$$\int_T \left(T_{\mu\nu}\, \xi^{\mu} \right)^{;\nu} \sqrt{-g}\, d^4x = \int_T \frac{\partial}{\partial x^{\nu}} \left(T_{\mu}{}^{\nu} \xi^{\mu} \sqrt{-g} \right) d^4x \tag{104}$$

gives a surface integral by Gauss' theorem which is zero because the ξ^{μ} are zero on the surface, the above equation becomes

$$- \int_T T^{\mu\nu}{}_{;\nu} \, \xi_\mu \sqrt{-g} \, d^4x = 0 . \tag{105}$$

Because the ξ_μ are arbitrary,

$$T^{\mu\nu}{}_{;\nu} = 0 . \tag{106}$$

The definition of $T^{\mu\nu}$ is thus consistent with Noether's theorem.

It is clear that the equations of other fields in a given gravitational field would be obtained by varying $\mathcal{L}_{total}$ with respect to the particular field variables with the $g_{\mu\nu}$ considered constant. This will lead to the same form of the field equations as we had in classical theory, except that all ordinary derivatives need to be replaced by covariant derivatives (involving $g_{\mu\nu}$). For example, if

$$\mathcal{L}_{total} = \mathcal{L}_g + \mathcal{L}_{em} \left(\mathcal{L}_{em} = \tfrac{1}{4} F_{\mu\nu} F^{\mu\nu}\right) \tag{107}$$

then

$$\delta \int_T \mathcal{L}_{total} \sqrt{-g} \, d^4x = 0 \tag{108}$$

gives

$$G_{\mu\nu} - \tfrac{1}{4}\left(F_{\mu\rho} F_\nu{}^\rho - \tfrac{1}{2} g_{\mu\nu} F_{\rho\sigma} F^{\rho\sigma}\right) = 0 \tag{109}$$

when the $g_{\mu\nu}$ are considered given and the A_μ vary; and

$$F^{\mu\nu}{}_{;\nu} = 0 \tag{110}$$

for the case when the $A_\nu(x)$ vary and the $g_{\mu\nu}$ are given.

Section V. EXACT SOLUTIONS AND APPROXIMATIONS

1. Coordinate Conditions

Previously we derived the gravitational field equations

$$\left(R_{\mu\nu} - \tfrac{1}{2} g_{\mu\nu} R\right) = aT_{\mu\nu},$$

or (111)

$$G_{\mu\nu} = aT_{\mu\nu},$$

and the conservation law for the stress-energy tensor $T^{\mu\nu}$:

$$T^{\mu\nu}{}_{;\nu} = 0. \tag{112}$$

We have also indicated that the field equations satisfy four identities

$$G^{\mu\nu}{}_{;\nu} = 0 \tag{113}$$

(as a consequence of the Bianchi identities), and thus are no longer a set of ten independent equations. However, if our field equations are to be covariant, four-dimensional, symmetric tensor equations, as above, it is necessary that they satisfy four differential identities so that we will be left with only six independent equations. This is seen when we notice that not all changes in $g_{\mu\nu}(x)$ are associated with changes in the space-time metric (i. e., with real changes in the gravitational field). Components of $g_{\mu\nu}$ also change under arbitrary transformation of coordinates in one and the same space-time. Since the coordinate transformations contain four arbitrary functions, by means of such transformations we can arbitrarily assign four of the components of $g_{\mu\nu}$. (The equations which assign in some noncovariant way four of the $g_{\mu\nu}$ $\left[\text{for example } g_{\mu 0} = \delta^0_\mu\right]$ are called coordinate conditions.) Therefore, there are only six independent components of $g_{\mu\nu}$. Thus it was concluded by Hilbert that the field equations should not be ten independent equations, but that four identities should hold such that we would have only six independent equations.[6,7] (Incidentally, it can be shown that the only tensor whose components depend on $g_{\mu\nu}$ only, and whose divergence vanishes (giving four auxiliary differential conditions) is the tensor $G^{\mu\nu}$.[6])

We will consider a spherically-symmetric gravitational field for which the equations can be solved exactly and illustrate the above notions in the process, but first we digress. We want to establish the connection between the Newtonian gravitational potential ϕ and the $g_{\mu\nu}$. For a nonrelativistic particle in a Newtonian gravitational field, the Lagrangian is

$$L = -mc^2 + \tfrac{1}{2}mv^2 - m\phi . \tag{114}$$

The equations of motion are given by Hamilton's principle:

$$\delta \left[-mc \int_{t_1}^{t_2} \left(c - \frac{1}{2}\frac{v^2}{c} + \frac{\phi}{c}\right)dt\right] = 0 , \tag{115}$$

or

$$\delta \left[-mc\int \left\{\left(c + \frac{\phi}{c}\right)dt - \frac{1}{2c}\ \vec{v}\cdot d\vec{r}\right\}\right] = 0 . \tag{116}$$

Now we have in the relativistic case for the motion of a particle

$$\delta \left[-mc \int_a^b ds\right] = 0$$

$$\left(\text{i. e.,}\ \delta \int_{t_1}^{t_2} L_{\text{matter}}\, dt = 0 \text{ with } ds = c\sqrt{1 - \beta^2}\ dt\right). \tag{117}$$

Thus, when we consider the case where a gravitational field is present and the $g_{\mu\nu}$ are given, we find the motion of a particle in the gravitational field by varying its path so that we obtain an extremum (or a geodesic). Now the space is "curved" and the geodesic "straight line" which the particle follows is:

$$mc\left(\frac{d^2x^\mu}{ds^2} + \Gamma^\mu_{\nu\kappa}\ \frac{dx^\nu}{ds}\ \frac{dx^\kappa}{ds}\right) = 0 . \tag{118}$$

This, of course, reduces in the absence of a gravitational field to the familiar

$$\frac{d}{dt}\left(\frac{m\vec{v}}{\sqrt{1 - \beta^2}}\right) = 0. \tag{119}$$

Now to correlate ϕ with the $g_{\mu\nu}$ we only need to go back to the action principle

$$\delta\left[-mc\int ds\right] = 0, \tag{120}$$

where we can see from Equation (116) that

$$ds = \left(c + \frac{\phi}{c}\right)dt - \frac{1}{2c}\,\vec{v}\cdot d\vec{r}. \tag{121}$$

Then neglecting terms in v^2/c^2 we find that

$$ds^2 = (c^2 + 2\phi)\,dt^2 - d\vec{r}^{\,2}, \tag{122}$$

so in the Newtonian limit

$$g_{\mu\nu} = \begin{pmatrix} 1+\frac{2\phi}{c^2} & 0 & 0 & 0 \\ 0 & -1 & 0 & 0 \\ 0 & 0 & -1 & 0 \\ 0 & 0 & 0 & -1 \end{pmatrix}; \tag{123}$$

$$\text{i.e.,}\quad g_{00} = 1 + \frac{2\phi}{c^2}.$$

2. The Schwarzschild Solution

The solution for a field of central symmetry (produced by centrally symmetric distributions of matter) was first obtained by Schwarzchild (1916). It is a particularly important solution in that we use it for the analysis of the three "positive" experiments mentioned earlier. Therefore, we shall derive this solution here.

In spherical coordinates r, θ, φ, the most general centrally-symmetric ds^2 is

$$\begin{aligned} ds^2 = {} & f_1(r,t)dr^2 + f_2(r,t)\,(\sin^2\theta\, d\varphi^2 + d\theta^2) \\ & + f_3(r,t)dt^2 + f_4(r,t)dr\,dt\,. \end{aligned} \tag{124}$$

The possibility of introducing four coordinate conditions for $g_{\mu\nu}$ implies that we can transform our $x^\nu \sim (r,\theta,\varphi,t)$ by any transformation that does not destroy the symmetry of ds^2, i.e., we can transform by

$$r = h_1(r',t'),\quad t = h_2(r',t') \tag{125}$$

in such a way that

$$f_2(r,t) \rightarrow -r^2, \quad f_4(r,t) \rightarrow 0. \tag{126}$$

NOTE: This condition does not determine t uniquely and we can still subject it to a transformation $t = f(t')$. By writing

$$\begin{aligned} f_1(r,t) &= -e^{\lambda(r,t)}, \\ f_3(r,t) &= c^2 e^{\nu(r,t)}, \end{aligned} \tag{127}$$

since they are just some nonsingular functions, we get

$$ds^2 = c^2 e^{\nu} dt^2 - r^2 (d\theta^2 + \sin^2\theta \, d\varphi^2) - e^{\lambda} dr^2, \tag{128}$$

or

$$g_{\mu\nu} = \begin{pmatrix} e^{\nu} & 0 & 0 & 0 \\ 0 & -e^{\lambda} & 0 & 0 \\ 0 & 0 & -r^2 & 0 \\ 0 & 0 & 0 & -r^2\sin^2\theta \end{pmatrix}. \tag{129}$$

Using the relation

$$\Gamma^{\nu}_{\kappa\lambda} = \frac{1}{2} g^{\nu\eta}\left(\frac{\partial g_{\eta\kappa}}{\partial x^{\lambda}} + \frac{\partial g_{\eta\lambda}}{\partial x^{\kappa}} - \frac{\partial g_{\kappa\lambda}}{\partial x^{\eta}}\right) \tag{130}$$

we find

$$\begin{aligned} \Gamma^1{}_{11} &= \frac{1}{2}\frac{\partial\lambda}{\partial r} & \Gamma^2{}_{33} &= -\sin\theta\cos\theta \\ \Gamma^1{}_{10} &= \frac{1}{2c}\frac{\partial\lambda}{\partial t} & \Gamma^1{}_{00} &= \frac{1}{2}\frac{\partial\nu}{\partial r} e^{\nu-\lambda} \\ \Gamma^2{}_{12} &= \Gamma^3{}_{13} = \frac{1}{r} & \Gamma^0{}_{00} &= \frac{1}{2c}\frac{\partial\nu}{\partial t} \\ \Gamma^0{}_{11} &= \frac{1}{2c}\frac{\partial\lambda}{\partial t} e^{\lambda-\nu} & \Gamma^3{}_{23} &= \cot\theta \end{aligned} \tag{131}$$

$$\Gamma^0{}_{10} = \frac{1}{2}\frac{\partial\nu}{\partial r}$$

$$\Gamma^1{}_{33} = -r\sin^2\theta\, e^{-\lambda}.$$

$$\Gamma^1{}_{22} = -re^{-\lambda}$$

Thus to write down our field equations we need to calculate

$$R_{\nu\kappa} = \frac{\partial\Gamma^\lambda_{\nu\kappa}}{\partial x^\lambda} - \frac{\partial\Gamma^\lambda_{\nu\lambda}}{\partial x^\kappa} + \Gamma^\lambda_{\nu\kappa}\Gamma^\eta_{\lambda\eta} - \Gamma^\eta_{\nu\lambda}\Gamma^\lambda_{\kappa\eta}. \tag{132}$$

By substituting from above and performing a lot of algebra, we finally get the only nonvanishing components of $G_\mu^{\ \nu}$:

$$G_0^{\ 0} = e^{-\lambda}\left(\frac{1}{r^2} - \frac{1}{r}\frac{\partial\lambda}{\partial r}\right) - \frac{1}{r^2}\ ; \tag{133}$$

$$G_0^{\ 1} = \frac{e^{-\lambda}}{rc}\frac{\partial\lambda}{\partial t}\ ; \tag{134}$$

$$\begin{aligned} G_2^{\ 2} = G_3^{\ 3} = \tfrac{1}{2}e^{-\lambda}&\left[\frac{\partial^2\nu}{\partial r^2} + \frac{1}{2}\left(\frac{\partial\nu}{\partial r}\right)^2 + \frac{1}{r}\left(\frac{\partial\nu}{\partial r} - \frac{\partial\lambda}{\partial r}\right) - \frac{1}{2}\frac{\partial\nu}{\partial r}\frac{\partial\lambda}{\partial r}\right] \\ -\tfrac{1}{2}e^{-\nu}&\left[\frac{1}{c^2}\frac{\partial^2\lambda}{\partial t^2} + \frac{1}{2c^2}\left(\frac{\partial\lambda}{\partial t}\right)^2 - \frac{1}{2c^2}\frac{\partial\lambda}{\partial t}\frac{\partial\nu}{\partial t}\right]\ ; \end{aligned} \tag{135}$$

$$G_1^{\ 1} = e^{-\lambda}\left(\frac{1}{r}\frac{\partial\nu}{\partial r} + \frac{1}{r^2}\right) - \frac{1}{r^2}\ . \tag{136}$$

These of course go to make up the energy-momentum tensor appearing in the equations

$$G_\mu^{\ \nu} = aT_\mu^{\ \nu}. \tag{137}$$

These equations can be integrated for the spherically-symmetric field in vacuum, i. e., outside of the symmetric mass distribution. In this region

$$T_\mu^{\ \nu} = 0, \tag{138}$$

and Equation (135) follows from the other three equations; so we have

$$e^{-\lambda}\left(-\frac{1}{r}\frac{\partial \lambda}{\partial r} + \frac{1}{r^2}\right) - \frac{1}{r^2} = 0 ,$$

$$e^{-\lambda}\left(\frac{1}{r}\frac{\partial \nu}{\partial r} + \frac{1}{r^2}\right) - \frac{1}{r^2} = 0 , \tag{139}$$

$$\frac{\partial \lambda}{\partial t} = 0 .$$

Thus λ is not time dependent. Also, from subtracting the first two equations we find that

$$\frac{\partial \lambda}{\partial r} + \frac{\partial \nu}{\partial r} = 0 , \tag{140}$$

or

$$\lambda + \nu = f(t) . \tag{141}$$

But earlier we stated that we still had the possibility of performing a transformation $t = f(t')$. We now choose $f(t) = 0$, so that

$$\lambda = -\nu .$$

Then both quantities are time-independent, and thus our gravitational field in vacuum (for this spherically symmetric case) is static.

Therefore, we have only to integrate

$$e^{-\lambda}\left(\frac{1}{r}\frac{\partial \lambda}{\partial r} - \frac{1}{r^2}\right) + \frac{1}{r^2} = 0 , \tag{142}$$

which gives

$$e^{-\lambda} = e^{\nu} = 1 + \frac{\text{const}}{r} = g_{00} . \tag{143}$$

However, we found that in the Newtonian approximation

$$g_{00} = 1 + \frac{2\phi}{c^2} . \tag{144}$$

Thus, our constant is given by

$$\text{const} = \frac{2km}{c^2}, \tag{145}$$

and

$$ds^2 = \left(c^2 - \frac{2km}{r}\right) dt^2 - r^2\left(\sin^2\theta\, d\varphi^2 + d\theta^2\right) - \frac{dr^2}{1 - \frac{2km}{c^2 r}}. \tag{146}$$

This is the Schwarzschild metric, and it completely determines the gravitational field outside a centrally symmetric mass distribution.

We notice that this solution has two singularities. One is at $r = 0$, and the second is at $r = \frac{2km}{c^2}$ and appears to limit the size of massive bodies to

$$r > 2\frac{km}{c^2}. \tag{147}$$

For an electron, this limiting radius is 13.2×10^{-56} cm. It is interesting to note that a charged spherical particle produces a metric[7]

$$ds^2 = \left(c^2 - \frac{2km}{r} + \frac{ke^2}{c^2 r^2}\right) dt^2$$

$$+ r^2 (\sin^2\theta\, d\varphi^2 + d\theta^2) \tag{148}$$

$$+ \frac{dr^2}{1 - \frac{2km}{c^2 r} + \frac{e^2 k}{c^4 r^2}}.$$

Einstein investigated a circularly uniform orbiting distribution of particles and showed that it is impossible to concentrate the particles to such a degree that the field has a singularity. (Annals of Mathematics <u>40</u>, 922 (1939).)

3. Weak Gravitational Fields and Gravitational Waves

By a weak field, we mean a field whose space-time is almost "flat" so that we can approximate our $g_{\mu\nu}$ by

$$g_{\mu\nu} = \overset{(0)}{g}_{\mu\nu} + h_{\mu\nu},$$

where (149)

$$g_{\mu\nu}^{(0)} = \begin{pmatrix} 1 & 0 & 0 & 0 \\ 0 & -1 & 0 & 0 \\ 0 & 0 & -1 & 0 \\ 0 & 0 & 0 & -1 \end{pmatrix}$$

and the $h_{\mu\nu}(x)$ are small corrections due to the gravitational field. If in our calculations we retain powers of $h_{\mu\nu}$ no higher than the first, then we find

$$R_{\nu\kappa\lambda\eta} = \frac{1}{2}\left(\frac{\partial^2 h_{\nu\eta}}{\partial x^\kappa \partial x^\lambda} + \frac{\partial^2 h_{\kappa\lambda}}{\partial x^\nu \partial x^\eta} - \frac{\partial^2 h_{\kappa\eta}}{\partial x^\nu \partial x^\lambda} - \frac{\partial^2 h_{\nu\lambda}}{\partial x^\kappa \partial x^\eta}\right) \tag{150}$$

and

$$R_{\nu\kappa} = g^{\lambda\eta} R_{\lambda\nu\eta\kappa} \approx g^{(0)\lambda\eta} R_{\lambda\nu\eta\kappa}$$

$$= \frac{1}{2}\left(-g^{(0)\lambda\eta} \frac{\partial^2 h_{\nu\kappa}}{\partial x^\lambda \partial x^\eta} + \frac{\partial^2 h_\nu{}^\lambda}{\partial x^\kappa \partial x^\lambda} + \frac{\partial^2 h_\kappa{}^\lambda}{\partial x^\nu \partial x^\lambda} - \frac{\partial^2 h_\eta{}^\eta}{\partial x^\nu \partial x^\kappa}\right). \tag{151}$$

Here again we can choose four coordinate conditions on $h_{\nu\kappa}$ provided they leave $h_{\nu\kappa}$ small. We choose these to be the following:

$$\frac{\partial h_\nu{}^\kappa}{\partial x^\kappa} = \frac{1}{2}\delta_\nu^\kappa \frac{\partial h_\lambda{}^\lambda}{\partial x^\kappa} ; \tag{152}$$

because of these the last three terms in $R_{\nu\kappa}$ above cancel each other, giving

$$R_{\nu\kappa} = -\frac{1}{2} g^{(0)\lambda\eta} \frac{\partial^2 h_{\nu\kappa}}{\partial x^\lambda \partial x^\eta} . \tag{153}$$

For a gravitational field in vacuum this is just

$$\Box h_{\nu\kappa} = 0, \tag{154}$$

where

$$\Box = \nabla^2 - \frac{1}{c^2}\frac{\partial^2}{\partial t^2} . \tag{155}$$

This is the ordinary wave equation. Of course the auxiliary conditions hold, but they now take the form

$$G^{\mu\nu}{}_{;\nu} = h^{\mu\nu}{}_{;\nu} = 0. \tag{156}$$

For the case where other fields give rise to a $T^{\mu\nu}$ we get:

$$\Box h_{\mu}{}^{\nu} = a T_{\mu}{}^{\nu}. \tag{157}$$

The solutions to this four-dimensional Poisson equation are known from electrodynamics:

$$h_{\mu}{}^{\nu}(\vec{r}, t) = \frac{1}{4\pi} \int \frac{(T_{\mu}{}^{\nu}) \text{ retarded}}{|\vec{r} - \vec{r}'|} d^3x' . \tag{158}$$

These are called "weak field" solutions of the gravitational equations.

LITERATURE CITED

1. J. W. Leech, CLASSICAL MECHANICS, London, Methuen and Co., 1958.

2. G. W. Bliss, LECTURES ON THE CALCULUS OF VARIATIONS, Chicago, Chicago University Press, 1946.

3. Landau and Lifshitz, THE CLASSICAL THEORY OF FIELDS, Reading, Mass., Addison-Wesley Publishing Co., 1959.

4. E. Noether, "Invariante Variationsprobleme," Göttinger Nachrichten, 211, 1918.

5. C. Møller (editor), EVIDENCE FOR GRAVITATIONAL THEORIES, New York, Academic Press, 1961.

6. P. G. Bergmann, AN INTRODUCTION TO THE THEORY OF RELATIVITY, New York, Prentice Hall, 1942.

7. J. Weber, GENERAL RELATIVITY AND GRAVITATIONAL WAVES, New York, Interscience, 1961.

THE MOSSBAUER EFFECT

by

AMBUJ MUKERJI*

and

C. A. COULTER, Editor

Solid State Physics Branch
Physical Sciences Laboratory
Research and Development Directorate
U. S. Army Missile Command
Redstone Arsenal, Alabama 35809

*Physics Department, University of Alabama.

ABSTRACT

The theory of the nuclear Mössbauer effect and its optical analogue is presented in this report. Introductory paragraphs deal with the destruction of resonance fluorescence in case of a freely recoiling nucleus. The partial restoration of resonance by Doppler effect and thermal broadening is outlined. The concept of zero-phonon transitions between bound nuclear states of nuclei embedded in a crystalline lattice is introduced in a simple quantum mechanical language. The classical derivation of the Debye-Waller factor based on the frequency modulation concept is followed by a rigorous quantum mechanical calculation of the zero-phonon transition probability and its temperature dependence. Lipkin's sum rule is discussed. Application of the Mössbauer effect to determine lifetimes of excited states, nuclear quadrupole moments, and the isomeric shifts is shown. The optical analogue in defect solids is described.

CONTENTS

1. Introduction

Resonant scattering of gamma rays is analogous to the well known phenomenon of resonance fluorescence in optics. Both the optical and nuclear resonance absorption may be explained in the following way. A quantum emitted in the transition from the excited state B to the ground state A induces the resonance absorption in an identical atom or nucleus. The atom or nucleus excited in such a manner

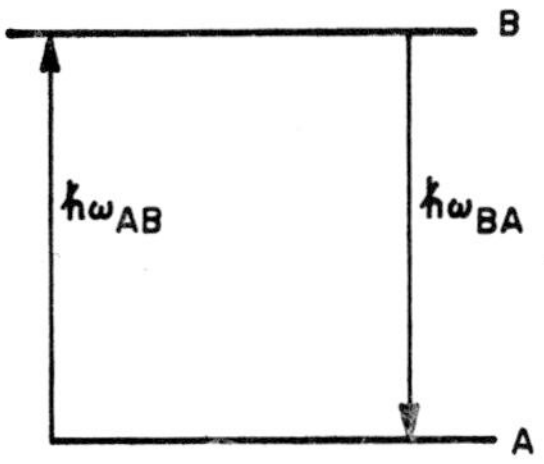

returns to the ground state with a decay constant characteristic of the excited level and a quantum of the same frequency is emitted. Processes of absorption and reemission are independent and no fixed phase relation exists between them. The resonant absorption results in gamma lines of the utmost narrowness,[1,2] which opens a wide range of applications in such fields as nuclear physics, solid state physics, and relativity, and makes possible investigations which could not even have been considered only a few years ago.[3]

2. Free Recoiling Nucleus

Problems in atomic and nuclear resonance seem very similar. However, marked differences make nuclear experiments much more difficult. Let us consider an isolated atom or nucleus of mass M, and let E^* and E be the energies of its excited and ground states, respectively.

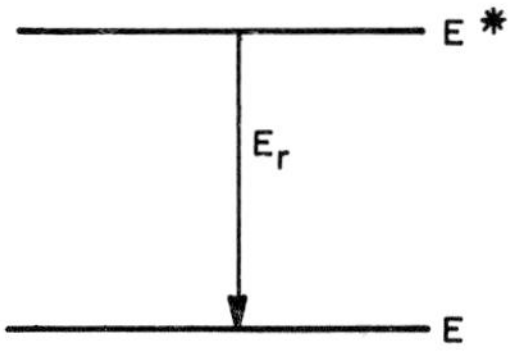

Let the quantities $\vec{P}$, $\vec{p}$, and E_r be defined as follows:

$\vec{P}$ = the momentum of the recoiling atom or nucleus;

$\vec{p}$ = the momentum of the radiated quantum;

$E_r = E^* - E$ = the energy separation of levels A and B.

From the conservation of momentum we have $\vec{p} = -\vec{P}$. Therefore, the recoil energy is

$$R = \frac{P^2}{2M} = \frac{p^2}{2M} = \frac{E_\gamma^2}{2Mc^2}, \tag{1}$$

where E_γ is the energy of the quantum emitted. Hence

$$E_r = E_\gamma + R. \tag{2}$$

If the gamma-ray energy is small compared to the rest mass energy, then $R \ll E_\gamma$ and

$$R \cong \frac{E_r^2}{2Mc^2}. \tag{3}$$

If the lifetime of the excited state is τ, the natural width of the emission line is given by $\Gamma\tau \geqslant \hbar$. For the nuclear transitions of interest in the Mössbauer effect, we have

$$10^{-10}\ \text{eV} < \Gamma < 10^{-4}\ \text{eV}.$$

Actual widths of the gamma lines greatly exceed Γ due to the Doppler broadening which arises because atoms in the source and the absorber are in thermal motion. Let us consider a source with initial momentum $\vec{P}_i$ which emits a photon of momentum $\vec{p}$. The momentum of the source after emission is $\vec{P}_i - \vec{p}$. Assume that the mass of the quantum system does not change during the emission. (Actually, there is a very small change in mass because the photon carries away some energy.) The energy gained by the source and, hence, lost by the gamma ray is

$$R' = \frac{\left(\vec{P}_i - \vec{p}\right)^2}{2M} - \frac{P_i^2}{2M}$$

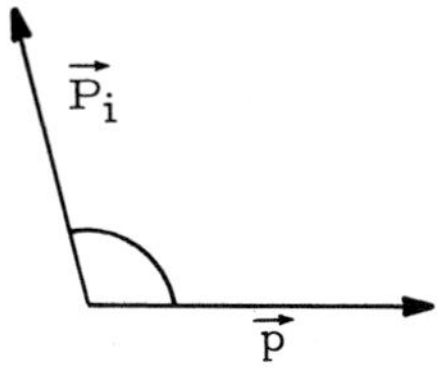

$$= \frac{P_i^2 + p^2 - 2\vec{P}_i \cdot \vec{p}}{2M} - \frac{P_i^2}{2M} \tag{4}$$

$$= \frac{p^2}{2M} - \frac{\vec{P}_i \cdot \vec{p}}{M} = R - D \cos\left(\vec{P}_i, \vec{p}\right). \tag{5}$$

Here

$$D = 2\,(\mathcal{E}R)^{1/2} ,$$

where $\mathcal{E} = \dfrac{P_i^2}{2M}$

is the kinetic energy of the quantum system before emission. The second term in the above equation is the Doppler shift. Therefore,

$$E_\gamma = E_r - R' = E_r - R + D \cos\left(\vec{P}_i, \vec{p}\right) . \tag{6}$$

Generally, the angle between $\vec{P}_i$ and $\vec{p}$ varies between 0 and 2π. Therefore, the Doppler term above causes a spread in E_γ of the order of D, which is proportional to the initial kinetic energy of the system. The Doppler widths at room temperature are of the order of 10^{-1} eV. For low-energy gamma transitions R lies characteristically in the range 10^{-3} eV < R < 10 eV. The relative positions of the gamma emission and absorption lines are shown in Figure 1.

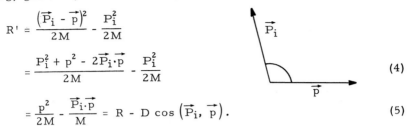

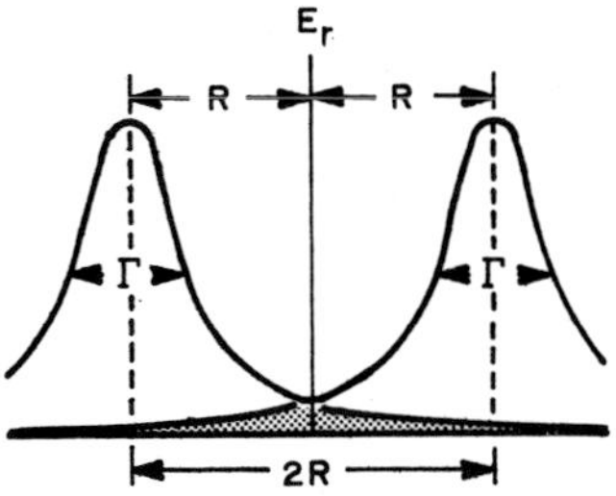

Figure 1. Overlap of Two Resonance Lines, Moved Apart as a Result of Recoil in Emission and Absorption

The difficulties encountered in the observation of the nuclear resonance absorption originate in the large separations of the gamma emission and absorption lines, which lead to unmeasurably small cross-sections for the resonance absorption process. Such problems do not exist in optical resonance absorption, where the low recoil energies involved cannot produce any appreciable separation of the two lines.

Prior to Mössbauer, all the methods used to observe nuclear resonant absorption had one common feature, which was that the linear Doppler effect was used to compensate by some means for the energy deficit connected with the recoil effect. Various methods tried were: (1) moving the source towards the resonant scatterer with an appropriate speed;[4] (2) heating the source and/or absorber to produce temperature broadening of lines; and (3) using the recoil momentum imparted in a preceding nuclear transition or in a nuclear reaction.[5]

3. Recoilless Gamma Transitions

The basic feature of the Mössbauer effect is the attainment of a complete energy resonance between identical types of emitting and absorbing nuclei. This is achieved by preventing these nuclei from picking up any recoil energy in the emission and absorption processes. In the absence of energy losses by recoil, the emission and absorption lines are no longer shifted away from each other, and their perfect overlap causes a large resonance effect. The recoil energy is given by

$$R = \frac{p^2}{2M} = \frac{E_\gamma^2}{2Mc^2} .$$

Therefore, R could be minimized by rigidly fastening the nuclei to an infinitely large mass. When the emitting nucleus is bound in a crystal lattice, the conservation of momentum still holds, i.e., $\vec{p} = -\vec{P}$. However, the momentum $\vec{P}$ is finally always taken up by the entire crystal. Because of the extremely large mass of the entire crystal in comparison with the nuclear mass, the translational motion of the crystal induced by the momentum transfer is negligible. Thus, momentum conservation is intrinsically fulfilled, and only the excitation and deexcitation of lattice vibrations, i.e., creation and annihilation of lattice phonons, need be considered. Under certain conditions, the constituent nuclei of a lattice may undergo transitions without accompanying creation or annihilation of phonons. These are termed zero-phonon or recoilless transitions. (It should be clearly understood that the term "recoilless" refers to the transfer of recoil energy rather than to the transfer of recoil momentum.)

The phenomenon of momentum transfer without simultaneous energy transfer was well known in other domains of physics long before Mössbauer, e.g., in coherent scattering of X rays (Rayleigh scattering and Bragg scattering), and the coherent scattering of slow neutrons in crystals.

The change ΔE_T in the translational energy of the crystal arising from the emission of a gamma quantum of momentum $\vec{p} = \hbar \vec{k}$ is given by

$$\Delta E_T = \frac{\left(\vec{p}_m - \hbar \vec{k}\right)^2}{2m} - \frac{p_m^2}{2m}$$

$$= \frac{\left(\hbar \vec{k}\right)^2}{2m} - \frac{\vec{p}_m \cdot \left(\hbar \vec{k}\right)}{m} , \qquad (7)$$

where $\vec{p}_m = \sum_j M_j \vec{V}_j$ is the center-of-mass momentum of the crystal, $\vec{V}_j$ is the velocity (in the laboratory system) of the j-th nucleus, and $m = \sum_j M_j$ is the total mass of the crystal. The total energy imparted to the crystal is given by

$$\Delta E = \frac{\left(\hbar \vec{k}\right)^2}{2M} - \frac{\vec{P}_i \cdot \left(\hbar \vec{k}\right)}{M} , \qquad (8)$$

where $\vec{P}_i$ is the initial momentum of the emitting nucleus and M is its mass. Therefore, the change in the internal energy of the crystal is

$$\Delta E_i = \Delta E - \Delta E_T$$

$$= \left[\frac{\left(\hbar \vec{k}\right)^2}{2M} - \frac{\left(\hbar \vec{k}\right)^2}{2m}\right] - \left[\vec{P}_i \cdot \frac{\hbar \vec{k}}{M} - \vec{p}_m \cdot \frac{\hbar \vec{k}}{m}\right] , \qquad (9)$$

and the total energy transfer depends upon the momentum $\vec{P}_i$ possessed by the nucleus at the time of gamma emission.

In the case of the freely recoiling nucleus this momentum could be determined, thus a well-defined relationship is provided between the momentum and the energy transfer to the nucleus. In the case of a bound nucleus, classical mechanics presents no barrier to a determination of the initial momentum of an emitting nucleus. However, quantum mechanics does not permit such a determination. The nucleus being bound in the crystal is limited in its movement to a region in space of the order of interatomic distances. Therefore, the uncertainty in momentum is

$$\Delta P_i \sim \frac{\hbar}{a} \sim 10^{-19} \text{ g cm s}^{-1},$$

where a is the interatomic distance in the crystal. However, to distinguish between recoilless and nonrecoilless processes, we require a knowledge of the initial momentum of the emitting nucleus to an accuracy of the order of

$$\Delta P_i \leqslant \frac{\Gamma M}{|\hbar \vec{k}|} \sim 10^{-24} \text{ g cm s}^{-1}$$

(taking $\Gamma = 10^{-10}$ eV). These two conditions on $\Delta\vec{P}_i$ are clearly incompatible. The uncertainty in the initial momentum $\vec{P}_i$ of the emitting nucleus leads to an uncertainty in the energy transferred to the lattice which is so large that it becomes impossible to classify a single emission process as recoilless or nonrecoilless. Quantum mechanics only permits the determination of probabilities for processes in which specific amounts of energy are transferred to the lattice. This is reflected by the fact that the final wave function Ψ of the crystal is no longer an eigenfunction of the crystal Hamiltonian, but rather a linear superposition of crystal eigenfunctions; that is,

$$\Psi = e^{-i\vec{k}\cdot\vec{x}}\, \psi_i = \sum_n c_n \psi_n \quad , \tag{10}$$

where the ψ_n are the eigenfunctions of the crystal Hamiltonian H_c:

$$H_c \psi_n = E_n \psi_n \,. \tag{11}$$

The operator $e^{-i\vec{k}\cdot\vec{x}}$ describes the transfer of momentum $-\hbar\vec{k}$ to the crystal, $\vec{x}$ being the position coordinate of the nucleus undergoing transition. It should be emphasized that the coefficients c_n occurring in Equation (10) are time-independent as long as we limit attention to times long compared to the decay time of the nucleus undergoing the gamma-ray transition. The choice of the particular operator $e^{-i\vec{k}\cdot\vec{x}}$ will be discussed later.

It will be shown now that the momentum of the system crystal-plus-photon is conserved independently of the details of the actual momentum transfer and any associated transfer times. The expectation value of the linear momentum with the crystal initially at rest is

$$\langle\Psi_i|\vec{p}_c|\Psi_i\rangle = \langle\Phi_i\,\phi_i|\vec{p}_m|\Phi_i\,\phi_i\rangle + \langle\Phi_i\,\phi_i|\sum_j \vec{P}_j|\Phi_i\,\phi_i\rangle \ . \qquad (12)$$

The total wave function Ψ_i of the crystal has been expressed as a product of two functions, one depending on the center-of-mass coordinates $\vec{x}_m$ of the entire crystal and the other on the relative positions $\vec{Q}_j$ of the individual nuclei. The operator representing the total internal momentum vanishes: $\sum_j \vec{P}_j = 0$. Hence, the momentum operator for the crystal is

$$\vec{p}_c = \vec{p}_m + \sum_j \vec{P}_j = \vec{p}_m. \qquad (13)$$

After the emission of a gamma quantum of momentum $\hbar\vec{k}$, we have

$$\langle\Psi|\vec{p}_c|\Psi\rangle = \langle e^{-i\vec{k}\cdot\vec{x}}\,\Phi_i\phi_i\,|\vec{p}_m|\,e^{-i\vec{k}\cdot\vec{x}}\,\Phi_i\,\phi_i\rangle \ . \qquad (14)$$

The position coordinate is $\vec{x} = \vec{x}_M + \vec{Q}$; therefore,

$$\langle\Psi|\vec{p}_c|\Psi\rangle = \langle\Psi|\vec{p}_m|\Psi\rangle = -\,\hbar\vec{k}. \qquad (15)$$

Thus, a momentum $-\hbar\vec{k}$, equal in magnitude but with direction opposite to that of the gamma quantum, is associated with the center-of-mass motion of the crystal. This is equivalent to the statement usually made that the momentum is taken up by the whole crystal.

Let us first assume that only a limited part of the crystal takes up the recoil momentum. Also assume that the lifetime involved in the gamma transition is $\tau = 10^{-7}$ second. During this time the disturbance travels a distance $L \sim \tau v$, where v is the velocity of sound in the crystal ($v \sim 10^5$ centimeters per second) and L is a linear dimension of the part of the crystal that classically has taken up the recoil momentum. Suppose that the mass of this portion of the crystal is

$$\mu = \left(\frac{L}{a}\right)^3 M,$$

where M is the mass of a single nucleus. This portion of the crystal oscillates as a whole with a frequency

$$\omega \sim \omega_L \left(\frac{a}{L}\right)^{3/2} ,$$

where ω_L is a typical lattice vibration frequency. The square of its zero-point momentum is given by

$$\begin{aligned} |p_\mu|^2 &\sim 2\mu \left(\frac{\hbar\omega}{4}\right) \\ &= 2\,\frac{L^3}{a^3}\,M\,\hbar\omega_L \left(\frac{a}{L}\right)^{3/2} \frac{1}{4} \\ &= \frac{1}{2}\left(\frac{L}{a}\right)^{3/2} M\,\hbar\omega_L \,. \end{aligned} \tag{16}$$

Now bear in mind that although the zero-point energy itself is precisely determined by the frequency ω_L, one has to attribute fluctuations to the kinetic and potential energy parts of the total zero-point energy which are of the order of the total zero-point energy itself. To obtain a sizeable probability for recoilless transitions, the transferred momentum must fulfill the condition

$$|\hbar\vec{k}|^2 \lessapprox M\,\hbar\omega_L \,.$$

Since $L \gg a$, we have a resulting uncertainty in the kinetic energy of the portion of the crystal under consideration which is of the order of

$$\frac{|p_\mu|^2}{2M} \gg \frac{(\hbar\vec{k})^2}{2M} ,$$

and it is not possible to verify by measurement that the recoil energy or momentum is actually carried by this portion of the crystal.

Also, the following observations can be made. A time of at least

$$\Delta t \sim \left(\frac{\hbar\,k^2}{2m}\right)^{-1}$$

is required to measure the recoil energy of the whole crystal (which is not bound, and therefore not subject to zero-point fluctuations). This time is given by

$$\Delta t \sim \frac{2m\hbar}{(\hbar \vec{k})^2} = 2\left(\frac{\ell}{a}\right)^3 M \frac{\hbar}{(\hbar \vec{k})^2}$$

$$\geq 2\left(\frac{\ell}{a}\right)^3 \omega_L^{-1} , \qquad (17)$$

where ℓ is the linear extension of the whole crystal. However, the time in which the sound waves reach the edge of the crystal is

$$\Delta t_s \simeq \frac{\ell}{v} \sim \frac{2\pi\ell}{a\omega_L} ,$$

so that

$$\frac{\Delta t}{\Delta t_s} \sim \pi^{-1} \left(\frac{\ell}{a}\right)^2 \gg 1.$$

Therefore, to measure the recoil energy of the crystal and to verify the conservation of energy will require a long time compared to the time necessary for the sound to propagate through the crystal. The mechanism by which the momentum is distributed throughout the crystal is not accessible to observation, and consequently the conclusion that the whole crystal takes up the momentum is not in conflict with the notion of a finite wave velocity of disturbances propagating through a crystal lattice.[6] These remarks apply only to the case where the zero-point energies associated with the vibrations of individual nuclei inside the crystal exceed or are comparable to the average recoil energy given to the crystal. This is the case which is of interest in the Mössbauer effect.

The previous discussion can be summarized in the following manner. The momentum is taken up by the whole crystal. The energy associated with the translational motion of the center-of-mass is negligible. The internal energy transitions, however, occur as phonon transitions between lattice oscillator states - which do not store momentum since the expectation value of the momentum operator for any oscillator state is zero. Therefore, the situation exists where the momentum is picked up by the whole crystal without a significant amount of accompanying energy going to the center-of-mass motion, while the energy is picked up by the lattice oscillators without any corresponding momentum transfer to the oscillators. In this sense, the momentum and energy may be considered as decoupled quantities.

4. Recoilless Resonance Absorption

An atom bound in a solid is confined to a region of space of linear extension ΔX smaller than a. Therefore,

$$\hbar|\Delta\vec{k}| \geq \frac{\hbar}{\Delta X} \quad .$$

In case the momentum $\hbar\vec{k}$ transferred to a crystal during a gamma transition is comparable to or smaller than $\hbar\Delta\vec{k}$, it is no longer possible to predict recoilless or nonrecoilless transitions in a single process. Therefore,

$$|\vec{k}| \leq \frac{1}{\Delta X}$$

is the prerequisite condition for the existence of a large probability for a recoilless transition. The sum rule due to Lipkin[7] states that on the average the recoil energy given to a nucleus bound in a crystal equals the recoil energy received by a free recoiling nucleus in a single process. Even classically, this relation can be seen to be true from the simpler considerations discussed earlier in Equation (8). The Doppler term vanishes if we average over a large ensemble of particles, leaving

$$\langle R\rangle_{av} = \frac{\hbar^2 k^2}{2M} \quad . \tag{18}$$

Let us consider the two limiting cases in which the average recoil energy $\langle R\rangle$ is either large or small compared to the transition energy of the Einstein oscillators:

Case i) $\langle R\rangle_{av} \gg \hbar\omega_E$;

Case ii) $\langle R\rangle_{av} \ll \hbar\omega_E$.

In case i) many transitions of Einstein oscillators are, on the average, required to transfer an energy of order $\langle R\rangle_{av}$ to the lattice. Consequently the probability of a nuclear transition taking place without a simultaneous phonon transition will be small. In case ii) nuclear transitions will only rarely be associated with simultaneous phonon transitions, which results in a high probability for recoilless transitions. The relative probability P for a gamma transition accompanied by simultaneous (one phonon) transitions of 0, 1, 2, ... n Einstein oscillators of frequency ω, at the temperature $T = 0$, illustrated for these two extreme values of the average energy transfer $\langle R\rangle_{av}$ is shown in Figures 2 and 3.[8]

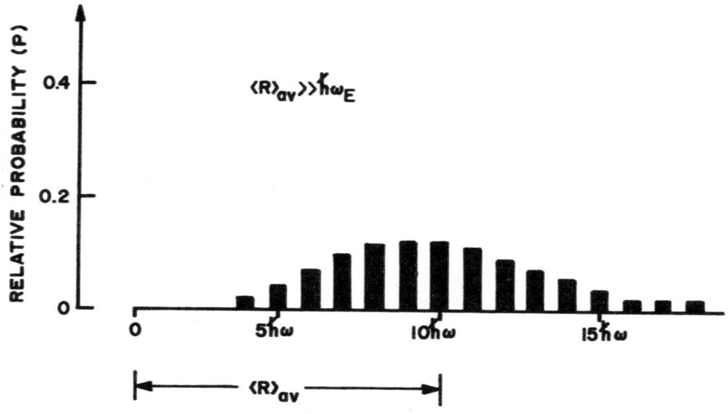

Figure 2. Relative Probability for a Gamma Transition Accompanied by Simultaneous Phonon Emission (Case i)

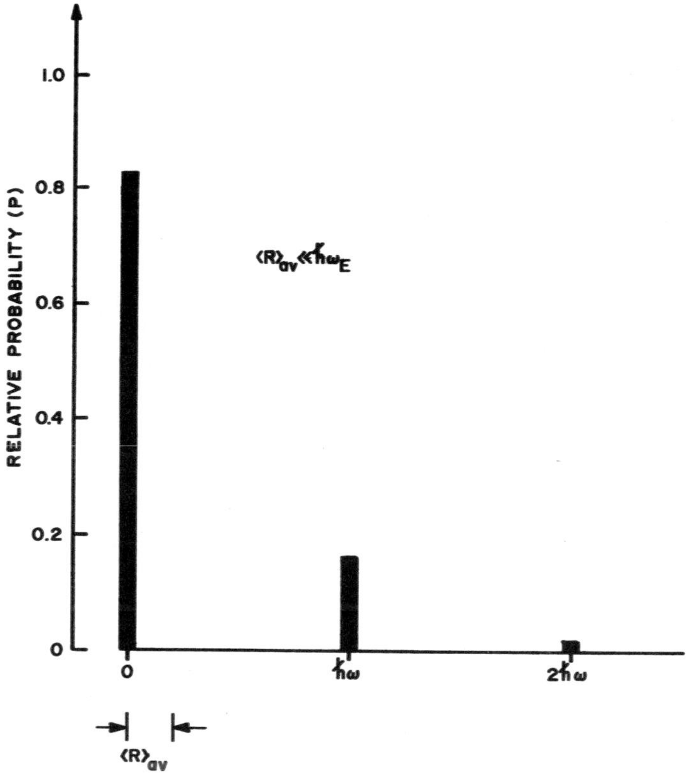

Figure 3. Relative Probability for a Gamma Transition Accompanied by Simultaneous Phonon Emission (Case ii)

These qualitative considerations apply equally well to a real crystal if the Einstein frequency ω_E is replaced by a characteristic frequency of the vibrational spectrum of the crystal, typically of the order of $k_B \Theta_D$, where Θ_D is the Debye temperature. The essential condition which leads to a high probability for recoilless gamma transition is

$$\frac{(\hbar \vec{k})^2}{2m} \lesssim k_B \Theta_D .$$

5. The Debye-Waller Factor: Classical Theory

The probability of recoilless emission is given by $P(n_i, n_i)$. The ensemble average of $P(n_i, n_i)$ is essentially equivalent to the Debye-Waller factor. While a quantitative description of recoilless nuclear transitions necessitates a quantum-mechanical treatment, some of the qualitative features may be obtained on simple semiclassical grounds. The existence of an unshifted line can, for instance, be deduced in a semiclassical treatment. Shapiro[9] has derived the Debye-Waller factor for the unshifted peak using a classical model in the case of a Debye spectrum, obtaining complete agreement with the quantum-mechanical calculations.

The vector potential of an electromagnetic wave emitted by a classical oscillator of constant frequency can be written as

$$\vec{A}(t) = \vec{A}_o \, e^{i\omega_o t},$$

where without loss of generality A_o is normalized so that

$$|A_o|^2 = 1 .$$

If the frequency is a function of time, this is replaced by

$$\vec{A}(t) = \vec{A}_o(0) \exp\left[i \int_0^t \omega(t')\, dt' \right]. \tag{19}$$

Assume for simplicity that the emitting oscillator moves in the X-direction with a velocity v(t') which is small compared to the velocity of light c. The frequency of the emitted wave is changed because of the Doppler effect:

$$\omega(t') = \omega_o \left[1 + \frac{v(t')}{c}\right] . \tag{20}$$

Inserting Equation (20) into Equation (19) gives

$$\vec{A} = \vec{A}_o \exp\left[i \int_o^t \omega_o \left(1 + \frac{v(t')}{c}\right) dt'\right]$$

$$= \vec{A}_o \exp i\omega_o t \exp\left[i \int_o^t \frac{\omega_o \, v(t')}{c} \, dt'\right]$$

$$= \vec{A}_o \exp i\omega_o t \exp\left(\frac{iX(t)}{\lambda\!\!\!^{-}}\right) . \tag{21}$$

The essential features can now be discussed by letting the source of the electromagnetic wave execute a simple harmonic motion with frequency Ω and amplitude X_o:

$$X(t) = X_o \sin \Omega t.$$

Then

$$\vec{A} = \vec{A}_o \exp\left(i\omega_o t\right) \exp\left(i \frac{X_o}{\lambda\!\!\!^{-}} \sin \Omega t\right) . \tag{22}$$

Such expressions are well known from the theory of frequency modulation in radio transmission. The spectrum, which originally just contained the carrier frequency ω_o, splits up into lines of frequencies ω_o, $\omega_o \pm \Omega$, $\omega_o \pm 2\Omega$ . . . . This splitting is derived by using the relation

$$\exp(i y \sin \theta) = \sum_{n=-\infty}^{\infty} J_n(y) \exp(in\theta).$$

By substituting this expansion one can write Equation (22) as

$$\vec{A} = \vec{A}_o \exp i\omega_o t \exp\left(i X_o \frac{\sin \Omega t}{\lambda\!\!\!^{-}}\right)$$

$$= \vec{A}_o \sum_{n=-\infty}^{\infty} \exp\left(i\omega_o t\right) J_n\left(\frac{X_o}{\lambda\!\!\!^{-}}\right) \exp\left(in\,\Omega t\right)$$

$$= \vec{A}_o \sum_{n=-\infty}^{\infty} J_n\left(\frac{X_o}{\lambda\!\!\!^{-}}\right) \exp i\left(\omega_o + n\Omega\right)t. \tag{23}$$

Equation (23) describes an electromagnetic wave which is a superposition of partial waves with frequencies ω_o, $\omega_o \pm \Omega$, $\omega_o \pm 2\Omega$, ... The amplitude of each wave is given by the Bessel function $J_n\left(\frac{X_o}{\lambda\!\!\!^{-}}\right)$. The unshifted line (n = 0) can be identified with the Mössbauer line. Its intensity is given by

$$f = |A(n=o)|^2 = J_o^2\left(\frac{X_o}{\lambda\!\!\!^{-}}\right). \tag{24}$$

Since A_o is normalized, f directly yields the probability of emission of the unshifted component.

Thus far it has been assumed that the emitted wave is modulated by one frequency only. Applied to solids, this corresponds to the Einstein model. For a real solid, the frequency Ω and the amplitude X_o are replaced by a sum over frequencies Ω_m with amplitudes X_m. Therefore, the intensity equation can be written as

$$f = \prod_{m=1}^{3N} J_o^2\left(\frac{X_m}{\lambda\!\!\!^{-}}\right). \tag{25}$$

The number 3N of frequencies in a solid is extremely large. Each of the factors J_o^2 in the above equation is only very slightly different from unity, since the maximum amplitude X_m of each individual frequency component is extremely small. Thus, J_o can be expanded,

$$J_o(y) = 1 - \frac{1}{4}y^2 + \cdots,$$

and

$$\ell n\, f = 2 \sum_m \ell n\, J_o \left(\frac{X_m}{\lambda\!\!\!^-} \right)$$

$$\simeq 2 \sum_m \ell n \left(1 - \frac{1}{4} \frac{X_m^2}{\lambda\!\!\!^-{}^2} \right)$$

$$\approx - 2 \sum_m \frac{1}{4} \left(\frac{X_m}{\lambda\!\!\!^-} \right)^2 \quad .$$

The mean square deviation of the vibrating atom from its equilibrium position is

$$\langle X^2 \rangle = \frac{1}{2} \sum_m X_m^2 \ ;$$

therefore,

$$\ell n\, f \simeq - \frac{\langle X^2 \rangle}{\lambda\!\!\!^-{}^2} \quad .$$

This equation is exact in the limit $N = \infty$. Therefore, the final result is

$$P\left(n_i,\ n_i\right) = f = \exp\left(- \frac{\langle X^2 \rangle}{\lambda\!\!\!^-{}^2} \right). \qquad (26)$$

The above equation can be given a simple interpretation. The continuously emitted electromagnetic wave comes from a region whose linear dimension is characterized by $\langle X^2 \rangle$. If this linear dimension increases beyond the wavelength $\lambda\!\!\!^-$, pieces of wave train emitted from different points in this region interfere destructively and the fraction f of photons emitted without energy loss decreases rapidly.

The wave train described by Equation (22) is infinitely long, and the corresponding emission line is infinitely narrow. For finite wave trains, the line becomes broadened. The Mössbauer line is then clearly recognizable only if the line width Γ is smaller than the separation from the first satellite, i. e., if

$$\Gamma < \hbar\Omega ,$$

or

$$\Omega > \frac{\Gamma}{\hbar} = \frac{1}{\tau} \ .$$

Therefore, the nuclear lifetime τ must be larger than the characteristic lattice time $\frac{1}{\Omega}$.

Figure 4 is based on an Einstein solid without any interaction among the various oscillators. In an actual solid only the unshifted line shows the natural width Γ; the satellites overlap each other and give rise to a continuum.

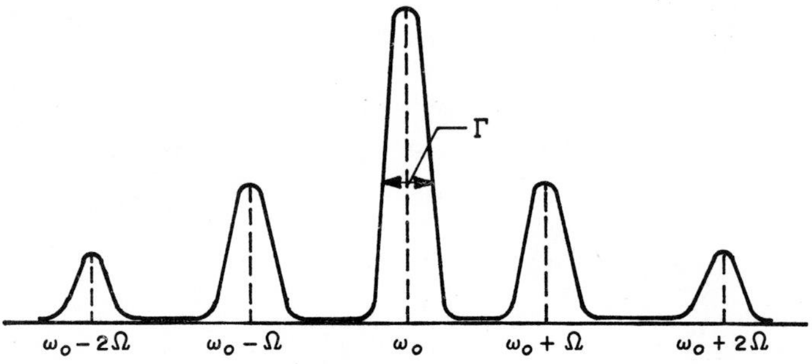

Figure 4. Spectrum of a Classical Electromagnetic Wave of Finite Length Emitted by an Einstein Solid

6. The Transition Matrix Elements

The transition matrix elements of the emission or absorption of a gamma ray by a free nucleus can be described by

$$M = \left\langle f \left| A\left(\vec{X}_i,\ \vec{P}_i,\ \vec{\sigma}_i\right) \right| i \right\rangle. \tag{27}$$

The operator A depends upon the coordinates, momenta, and spins of the particles in the nucleus. Let us now express the operator A in terms of the center-of-mass coordinates of the nucleus $\vec{x}$ and a set of coordinates q which include spins. The dependence of A upon $\vec{x}$ is determined by the requirements that the momentum should be conserved and that the transition probability for a moving observer (nonrelativistic) should not depend on the velocity of the observer. For the emission of a gamma ray of momentum $\hbar \vec{k}$, the above requirements are satisfied only if

$$A = \exp\left(i\vec{k}\cdot\vec{x}\right) a(q) \quad . \tag{28}$$

The explicit form of the operator a(q) is of no interest to us in the present discussion. It depends on the relative variables and spins of the particles, and has an explicit form depending upon the nature of the radiation.

When the nucleus is bound in a crystal, the operator describing the transition is the same operator A; but we must now take the matrix element between initial and final states of the whole lattice rather than of the free nucleus. Since the nuclear forces are much stronger than the crystal forces, we can assume that the binding forces act only upon the center-of-mass motion of the nucleus and do not perturb the internal degrees of freedom. Therefore, the matrix element for a transition in which a gamma ray of momentum $\hbar \vec{k}$ is emitted by a nucleus whose center-of-mass coordinate is $\vec{x}$, while the lattice goes from a state specified by quantum numbers n_i to a state specified by quantum numbers n_f and the internal state of the emitting nucleus changes from $|i\rangle$ to $\langle f|$, is

$$M_L = \langle n_f | \exp\left(i \vec{k}\cdot\vec{x}\right) | n_i \rangle \langle f | a(q) | i \rangle \quad . \tag{29}$$

The transition probability is proportional to the square of the matrix element. The dependence of the density of the final states of the emitted gamma ray upon the energy transfer to the lattice is neglected, since the gamma-ray energy is greater than the lattice energies by a factor of at least 10^5. We are not interested in the absolute transition rate, but in the relative probability of different energy transfers to the lattice. Therefore, we are interested in the probability $P(n_f,\ n_i)$ that the lattice will be in a particular state $\langle n_f|$ after the transition if it is initially in the state $|n_i\rangle$:

$$P\left(n_f,\ n_i\right) = \text{const} \left| \langle n_f | \exp i\, \vec{k}\cdot\vec{x} | n_i \rangle \right|^2 . \tag{30}$$

Imposing the normalization condition upon the probabilities, we have

$$\sum_f P\left(n_f,\ n_i\right) = 1.$$

Also

$$\sum_f P\left(n_f,\ n_i\right) = \text{const} \sum_f \langle n_i | \exp\left(-\, i \vec{k}\cdot\vec{x}\right) | n_f \rangle \langle n_f | \exp\left(i\, \vec{k}\cdot\vec{x}\right) | n_i \rangle$$
$$= \text{const} \langle n_i | \exp\left(-\, i\, \vec{k}\cdot\vec{x}\right) \exp\left(i\, \vec{k}\cdot\vec{x}\right) | n_i \rangle ,$$

or

$$\sum_f P\left(n_f,\ n_i\right) = \text{const} \langle n_i | n_i \rangle = 1.$$

Therefore, the value of the constant is one, and thus,

$$P(n_f, n_i) = \left|\langle n_f \left| \exp\left(i \vec{k} \cdot \vec{x}\right) \right| n_i \rangle\right|^2 . \tag{31}$$

The dependence of the matrix element M_L upon the nuclear-structure matrix element $\langle f | a(q) | i \rangle$ occurs as a common factor for all lattice states, and has been dropped in calculating the relative probability.

7. Lipkin's Sum Rule

Reference was made in Section 4 to Lipkin's sum rule,[7] which asserts that the average energy transferred to the lattice in photon emission is just the energy which the individual nucleus would have if it recoiled freely. We shall now prove this theorem.

If the binding forces of the crystal depend only on the positions of the atoms and not on their velocities, then the only term in the Hamiltonian H of the crystal which does not commute with x is the kinetic energy $p^2/2M$ of the same nucleus. We will make use of the following commutation relations:

$$\left[f\left(\vec{x}\right), \vec{p}\right] = i\hbar \nabla f\left(\vec{x}\right) \equiv i\hbar \text{ grad } f\left(\vec{x}\right)$$

and

$$\left[f\left(\vec{x}\right), p^2\right] = 2i\hbar\left(\nabla f\left(\vec{x}\right)\right) \cdot \vec{p} + \hbar^2 \nabla^2 f\left(\vec{x}\right) . \tag{32}$$

If

$$f\left(\vec{x}\right) = e^{(\pm)i \vec{k} \cdot \vec{x}} ,$$

the first commutator is

$$\left[e^{(\pm)i \vec{k} \cdot \vec{x}}, \vec{p}\right] = (\mp)\hbar \vec{k}\, e^{(\pm)i \vec{k} \cdot \vec{x}} .$$

Therefore,

$$\left[p^2, e^{(\pm)i \vec{k} \cdot \vec{x}}\right] = -\left[e^{(\pm)i \vec{k} \cdot \vec{x}}, p^2\right] = e^{(\pm)i \vec{k} \cdot \vec{x}}\left((\pm)\, 2\hbar\, \vec{k} \cdot \vec{p} + \hbar^2 k^2\right),$$

and for $H = \frac{p^2}{2M}$ plus a part which commutes with $e^{(\pm)i\vec{k}\cdot\vec{x}}$, we have

$$\left[H,\ e^{(\pm)i\vec{k}\cdot\vec{x}}\right] = \left[\frac{p^2}{2M},\ e^{(\pm)i\vec{k}\cdot\vec{x}}\right] = \frac{1}{2M}\ e^{(\pm)i\vec{k}\cdot\vec{x}}\left((\pm)2\hbar\,\vec{k}\cdot\vec{p} + \hbar^2 k^2\right) .$$

It follows that

$$\left[\left[H,\ e^{(\pm)i\vec{k}\cdot\vec{x}}\right],\ e^{(\mp)i\vec{k}\cdot\vec{x}}\right] = -\frac{\hbar^2 k^2}{M} . \tag{33}$$

By expanding the double commutator explicitly we also have

$$\left[\left[H,\ e^{(\pm)i\vec{k}\cdot\vec{x}}\right],\ e^{(\mp)i\vec{k}\cdot\vec{x}}\right] = \left[\left(H\ e^{(\pm)i\vec{k}\cdot\vec{x}} - e^{(\pm)i\vec{k}\cdot\vec{x}}H\right),\ e^{(\mp)i\vec{k}\cdot\vec{x}}\right]$$

$$= \left[H\ e^{(\pm)i\vec{k}\cdot\vec{x}},\ e^{(\mp)i\vec{k}\cdot\vec{x}}\right] - \left[e^{(\pm)i\vec{k}\cdot\vec{x}}H,\ e^{(\mp)i\vec{k}\cdot\vec{x}}\right]$$

$$= 2H - e^{(\mp)i\vec{k}\cdot\vec{x}}\,H\,e^{(\pm)i\vec{k}\cdot\vec{x}} - e^{(\pm)i\vec{k}\cdot\vec{x}}\,H\,e^{(\mp)i\vec{k}\cdot\vec{x}} . \tag{34}$$

Now writing the ii diagonal matrix element of Equation (34) in the representation in which the phonon populations are diagonal, we have

$$\langle n_i|\left[\left[H,\ e^{i\vec{k}\cdot\vec{x}}\right],\ e^{-i\vec{k}\cdot\vec{x}}\right]|n_i\rangle$$

$$= 2\langle n_i|H|n_i\rangle - \sum_{f,f'}\Big\{\langle n_i|e^{i\vec{k}\cdot\vec{x}}|n_f\rangle\langle n_f|H|n_{f'}\rangle\langle n_{f'}|e^{-i\vec{k}\cdot\vec{x}}|n_i\rangle$$

$$+ \langle n_i|e^{-i\vec{k}\cdot\vec{x}}|n_f\rangle\langle n_f|H|n_{f'}\rangle\langle n_{f'}|e^{i\vec{k}\cdot\vec{x}}|n_i\rangle\Big\}$$

$$= 2\langle n_i|H|n_i\rangle - \sum_{f,f'}\Big\{\langle n_i|e^{i\vec{k}\cdot\vec{x}}|n_f\rangle\langle n_{f'}|e^{-i\vec{k}\cdot\vec{x}}|n_i\rangle\langle n_f|H|n_{f'}\rangle$$

$$+ \langle n_i|e^{-i\vec{k}\cdot\vec{x}}|n_f\rangle\langle n_{f'}|e^{i\vec{k}\cdot\vec{x}}|n_i\rangle\langle n_f|H|n_{f'}\rangle\Big\}$$

$$= 2\langle n_i|H|n_i\rangle - 2\sum_{ff'}\langle n_i|e^{-i\vec{k}\cdot\vec{x}}|n_f\rangle\overline{\langle n_i|e^{-i\vec{k}\cdot\vec{x}}|n_{f'}\rangle}\langle n_f|H|n_{f'}\rangle\delta(ff')$$

$$= 2\left[E_{n_i} - \sum_f P(n_f,\ n_i)\,E_{n_f}\right] = 2\sum_f\left(E_{n_i} - E_{n_f}\right)P(n_f,\ n_i) .$$

In the last line of the previous equation, the result of Equation (31) was used, and E_{n_f} and E_{n_i} are the energies of the states n_f and n_i. Therefore, from Equation (33) we see that

$$\sum_f \left(E_{n_f} - E_{n_i}\right) P\left(n_f, n_i\right) = \frac{\hbar k^2}{2M} . \tag{35}$$

However, the average energy $\bar{R}$ transferred to the lattice is defined by

$$\bar{R} = \sum_f P\left(n_f, n_i\right) \left(E_{n_f} - E_{n_i}\right) . \tag{36}$$

Therefore,

$$\bar{R} = \frac{\hbar^2 k^2}{2M} = R , \tag{37}$$

where R is exactly the free-nucleus recoil energy (as shown earlier).

8. Quantum-Mechanical Derivation of the Debye-Waller Factor

The simplest problem is that of emission in a crystal lattice at absolute zero. We assume that the crystal binding is purely harmoni We introduce normal coordinates for a Bravais lattice of N identical atoms of mass M. If $\vec{x}_{ok}$ is the equilibrium position of the k-th nucleus, then

$$\vec{x}_k = \vec{x}_{ok} + \vec{u}_k, \tag{38}$$

where $\vec{u}_k$ is the displacement from equilibrium positon. A Fourier expansion of the displacement vectors $\vec{u}_k$ of the N nuclei in the lattice in terms of the 3N normal modes characterized by the unit polarization vector $e_{\vec{q}j}$ (for the propagation vector $\vec{q}$ and the polarization j) and the frequencies $\omega_{\vec{q}j}$ may be made. Replacing the pair of indices $(\vec{q}, j)$ by the single index s, we have[10]

$$\vec{u}_k = \sum_s \left[\frac{\hbar}{2MN\omega_s}\right]^{1/2} \vec{e}_s \left[a_{ks}(t)\, e^{i\vec{q}_s \cdot \vec{x}_{ok}} + a^+_{ks}(t)\, e^{-i\vec{q}_s \cdot \vec{x}_{ok}}\right], \tag{39}$$

where $\vec{e}_s$ is independent of k. The a^+ and a are the phonon creation and annihilation operators. Simplify the notation by setting

$$\vec{x}_{ok} = 0.$$

Then

$$\vec{u}_k = \sum_s \left[\frac{\hbar}{2MN\omega_s}\right]^{1/2} \vec{e}_s \left[a_{ks}(t) + a_{ks}^+(t)\right]$$

$$= \sum_s \left[\frac{\hbar}{2MN\omega_s}\right]^{1/2} \vec{e}_s \left(a_{ks}\, e^{-i\omega_s t} + a_{ks}^+\, e^{i\omega_s t}\right). \tag{40}$$

We shall drop the subscript k from now on. Note that Equation (40) may be written as

$$\vec{u} = N^{-1/2} \sum_s Q_s \vec{e}_s \quad , \tag{41}$$

where Q_s, the amplitude of the normal mode s, is given as

$$Q_s = \left(\frac{\hbar}{2M\omega_s}\right)^{1/2} \left[a_s(t) + a_s^+(t)\right] . \tag{42}$$

The associated momentum is

$$P_s = M\dot{Q}_s = -i\, M\omega_s \left(\frac{\hbar}{2M\omega_s}\right)^{1/2} \left(a_s\, e^{-i\omega_s t} - a_s^+\, e^{i\omega_s t}\right). \tag{43}$$

The Hamiltonian for the normal modes is

$$H = \frac{1}{2} \sum_s \left\{\frac{1}{M} P_s^2 + M\omega_s^2 Q_s^2\right\} . \tag{44}$$

The normalized ground-state wave function in the coordinate representation for the mode s is just the harmonic oscillator result

$$\langle x | 0_s \rangle = \frac{1}{\sqrt[4]{\pi}} \sqrt{a_s}\; e^{-a_s^2 Q_s^2/2} \quad , \tag{45}$$

where $a_s^2 = M\omega_s$. The probability of recoilless emission from the ground state is

$$P(0, 0) = \left|\langle 0 | e^{i\vec{k}\cdot\vec{u}} | 0 \rangle\right|^2$$

$$= \left|\prod_s \langle 0_s | e^{i\vec{k}\cdot\vec{e}_s Q_s N^{-1/2}} | 0_s \rangle\right|^2 , \tag{46}$$

where 0 signifies that all the lattice oscillators are in their ground states. Therefore,

$$P(0, 0) = \left|\prod_s \left\{\frac{\alpha_s}{\sqrt{\pi}} \int_{-\infty}^{+\infty} e^{-\alpha_s^2 Q_s^2} e^{i\beta_s Q_s} dQ_s\right\}\right|^2 , \tag{47}$$

where $\beta_s = \left(\vec{k}\cdot\vec{e}_s\right) N^{-1/2}$. The quantity within the brace in Equation (47) has the value $\exp\left(-\frac{\beta_s^2}{4\alpha_s^2}\right)$. Hence

$$P(0, 0) = \left|\prod_s e^{-\beta_s^2/4\alpha_s^2}\right|^2 . \tag{48}$$

For the ground state, we have

$$\langle Q_s^2 \rangle = \langle 0_s | Q_s^2 | 0_s \rangle = \frac{1}{2\alpha_s^2} . \tag{49}$$

From Equations (48) and (49) we have

$$P(0, 0) = \prod_s e^{-\beta_s^2 \langle Q_s^2 \rangle} = \prod_s e^{-\left(N^{-1}\right)\left(\vec{k}\cdot\vec{e}_s\right)^2 \langle Q_s^2 \rangle}$$

$$= e^{-\left(N^{-1}\right) \sum_s \left(\vec{k}\cdot\vec{e}_s\right)^2 \langle Q_s^2 \rangle} . \tag{50}$$

If $\langle Q_s^2 \rangle$ is assumed to be independent of the polarization j, then the following can be written:

$$\sum_j \left(\vec{k}\cdot\vec{e}_s\right)^2 \langle Q_s^2 \rangle = k^2 \langle Q_q^2 \rangle , \tag{51}$$

and

$$P(0, 0) = e^{-\left(N^{-1}\right) \sum_q k^2 \langle Q_q^2 \rangle} . \tag{52}$$

From Equation (41) we have

$$\vec{u} = N^{-1/2} \sum_s Q_s \vec{e}_s ,$$

so

$$\langle u^2 \rangle = \frac{1}{N} \sum_s \langle Q_s^2 \rangle = \frac{3}{N} \sum_q \langle Q_q^2 \rangle \tag{53}$$

and finally,

$$P(0, 0) = e^{-k^2 \langle u^2 \rangle /3} . \tag{54}$$

By the properties of Hermite polynomials, the identical result follows for a harmonic system not in the ground state of all phonons, but with the phonons in a canonical distribution. Therefore, the probability of recoilless emission with the phonons distributed according to a canonical distribution at temperature T is

$$f = P(n_T, n_T) = \exp\left[-\frac{1}{3} k^2 \langle u^2 \rangle_T\right]. \tag{55}$$

This is the Debye-Waller factor, and is designated customarily by e^{-2W}.

The Debye-Waller factor can easily be expressed in a different form if the virial theorem is used for the mean value of the potential energy of a harmonic oscillator:

$$\left(n_s + \frac{1}{2}\right) \hbar = M \omega_s \langle Q_s^2 \rangle. \tag{56}$$

We have

$$k^2 \langle u^2 \rangle = N^{-1} k^2 \sum_s \langle Q_s^2 \rangle = \frac{k^2}{2M} \frac{2}{N} \sum_s \frac{\left(n_s + \frac{1}{2}\right)\hbar}{\omega_s} ,$$

or

$$k^2 \langle u^2 \rangle = \frac{\hbar^2 k^2}{2M} \frac{2}{N\hbar} \sum_s \frac{\left(n_s + \frac{1}{2}\right)}{\omega_s} .$$

Now the free-atom recoil energy is

$$R = \frac{\hbar^2 k^2}{2M} \quad ;$$

hence

$$k^2 \langle u^2 \rangle = \frac{2R}{N\hbar} \sum_s \frac{n_s + \frac{1}{2}}{\omega_s} \quad . \tag{57}$$

At absolute zero $n_s = 0$ and we have

$$k^2 \langle u^2 \rangle = \frac{R}{N\hbar} \sum_s \omega_s^{-1} \quad . \tag{58}$$

For a Debye solid $\omega = vq$, where v is the velocity of sound and q is the wave vector. We note that

$$\frac{1}{3} \frac{1}{N} \sum_s q_s^{-1}$$

is just the mean value of $1/q$ over the 3N phonon modes. Therefore,

$$\frac{1}{3} \frac{1}{N\hbar} \sum_s q_s^{-1} = \hbar^{-1} \frac{\int_0^{q_{max}} dq\, q}{\int_0^{q_{max}} dq\, q^2} = \frac{3}{2} \frac{1}{\hbar\, q_{max}}$$

$$= \frac{3v}{2\hbar\omega_m} = \frac{3v}{2 k_B \Theta_D} \quad , \tag{59}$$

where Θ_D is the Debye temperature (defined as $\Theta_D = \hbar\,\omega_m / k_B$) and k_B is the Boltzmann constant. Hence, from Equations (54), (58), and (59) one finds

$$f(0) = P(0,\ 0) = e^{-3R/2k_B \Theta_D} \quad . \tag{60}$$

Thus, the fraction of recoilless events at absolute zero is substantial if the free-atom recoil energy is less than the maximum possible phonon energy.

At a nonzero temperature T,

$$\frac{1}{3} k^2 \langle u^2 \rangle_T = \frac{2R}{3N\hbar} \sum_s \frac{n_s + \frac{1}{2}}{\omega_s} . \tag{61}$$

Carry out the averaging over the initial states, replacing n_s by $\bar{n}_s$;

$$\bar{n}_s = \frac{\sum_{n_s} n_s e^{-n_s \hbar\omega_s/k_B T}}{\sum_{n_s} e^{-n_s \hbar\omega_s/k_B T}} = \frac{1}{e^{\hbar\omega_s/k_B T} - 1} . \tag{62}$$

Substitute this value into Equation (61) and replace the summation by an integral, introducing the density of vibrational states $\rho(\omega)$. Then, for a crystal of cubic symmetry the following can be written:

$$\frac{1}{3} k^2 \langle u^2 \rangle_T = \frac{2R}{3N\hbar} \int_0^{\omega_m} \left[\frac{1}{2} + \frac{1}{e^{\hbar\omega/k_B T} - 1} \right] \frac{\rho(\omega)}{\omega} d\omega \tag{63}$$

For a Debye solid, the density of states of the vibrational spectrum is given by

$$\rho(\omega) = \frac{9 N \omega^2}{\omega_m^3} , \tag{64}$$

which is normalized so that

$$\int_0^{\omega_m} \rho(\omega)\, d\omega = 3N . \tag{65}$$

Substituting the value of $\rho(\omega)$ given in Equation (64) into Equation (63), we get

$$\frac{1}{3} k^2 \langle u^2 \rangle_T = \frac{2R}{3N\hbar} \int_0^{\omega_m} \left[\frac{1}{2} + \frac{1}{e^{\hbar\omega/k_B T} - 1} \right] \frac{9N\omega}{\omega_m^3} d\omega . \tag{66}$$

Equation (66) can be simplified into

$$\frac{1}{3} k^2 \langle u^2 \rangle_T = \frac{6R}{\hbar \omega_m^3} \int_0^{\omega_m} \left[\frac{1}{2} + \frac{1}{e^{\hbar\omega/k_B T} - 1} \right] \omega \, d\omega \;. \tag{67}$$

By writing $\hbar \omega_m = k_B \Theta_D$ and $x = \frac{\hbar\omega}{k_B T}$ we get

$$\frac{1}{3} k^2 \langle u^2 \rangle_T = \left(\frac{k_B T}{\hbar}\right)^2 \frac{6R}{\hbar \omega_m^3} \int_0^{\Theta_D/T} \left[\frac{1}{2} + \frac{1}{e^x - 1} \right] x \, dx. \tag{68}$$

Carrying out the integration in the term containing the factor ½ yields

$$\frac{1}{3} k^2 \langle u^2 \rangle_T = \left(\frac{k_B T}{\hbar}\right)^2 \frac{6R}{\hbar \omega_m^3} \left[\frac{x^2}{4} \Bigg|_0^{\Theta_D/T} + \int_0^{\Theta_D/T} \frac{x \, dx}{e^x - 1} \right]$$

$$= \left(\frac{k_B T}{\hbar}\right)^2 \frac{3R}{2k_B \Theta_D} \frac{\Theta_D^2}{\omega_m^2 T^2} \left[1 + \frac{4T^2}{\Theta_D^2} \int_0^{\Theta_D/T} \frac{x \, dx}{e^x - 1} \right]$$

$$= \frac{3R}{2k_B \Theta_D} \left[1 + \frac{4T^2}{\Theta_D^2} \int_0^{\Theta_D/T} \frac{x \, dx}{e^x - 1} \right] . \tag{69}$$

For temperatures much lower than the Debye temperature, i.e., for $T \ll \Theta_D$, the upper limit of the integral in Equation (69) can be taken as infinity. Therefore, we get

$$\int_0^{\infty} \frac{x \, dx}{e^x - 1} = \frac{\pi^2}{6} \;. \tag{70}$$

With the help of Equation (70), Equation (69) can be written as

$$\frac{1}{3} k^2 \langle u^2 \rangle_T = \frac{3R}{2k_B \Theta_D} \left[1 + \frac{2}{3} \pi^2 \left(\frac{T}{\Theta_D} \right)^2 \right] . \qquad (71)$$

This expression inserted into Equation (55) gives the fraction of the recoilless transition at temperatues much lower than the Debye temperature $\left(T \ll \Theta_D\right)$ as

$$f = P\left(n_T, n_T\right) = e^{-2W} = \exp \left\{ - \frac{3R}{2k_B \Theta_D} \left[1 + \frac{2\pi^2}{3} \left(\frac{T}{\Theta_D} \right)^2 \right] \right\} . \qquad (72)$$

This is known as the Debye-Waller factor. In the limit of low temperature, this factor depends only on the ratio of the free-atom recoil energy to the Debye temperature:

$$f_0 = P\left(n_0, n_0\right) = \exp \left[- \frac{3R}{2k_B \Theta_D} \right]$$

$$= \exp \left[- \frac{3E_\gamma^2}{4Mc^2 k_B \Theta_D} \right] . \qquad (73)$$

Characteristic values for f are 0.91 for the 14.4 keV gamma ray of Fe^{57} and 0.06 for the 129 keV gamma ray of Ir^{191}, both for the natural metallic host lattice at liquid nitrogen temperature.

For a symmetry of the surroundings which is lower than cubic, the Debye-Waller factor depends on the angle between the direction of the momentum transfer and the crystal axis.

The increase in the rigidity experienced by a lattice upon application of pressure leads to an increase in the number of recoilless processes.

The analogies between the recoilless processes involved in X-ray scattering and the Mössbauer effect are to be noted. The essential similarity lies in the appearance of the mean square deviation of the radiating or scattering atom from its equilibrium position. The main difference lies in the times involved. X-ray scattering is "fast"; the characteristic time involved is much shorter than the characteristic lattice time. In contrast, the emission and scattering of gamma rays in the Mössbauer effect is "slow"; the relevant time is comparable to, or longer than, the characteristic lattice time.

9. Some Applications of the Mössbauer Effect in Nuclear and Solid State Physics

a. Lifetime of a Nuclear Level

The total line width Γ is found by tracing out the absorption and the scattering lines, using the Doppler effect. The ratio of the scattering and the absorption cross sections yields $\frac{\Gamma_\gamma}{\Gamma}$, where Γ_γ is the width due to the unconverted part of the gamma ray:

$$\sigma_{scatt}(E) = \sigma_o \frac{\Gamma_\gamma^2}{4(E - E_r)^2 + \Gamma^2} , \tag{74}$$

$$\sigma_{abs}(E) = \sigma_o \frac{\Gamma \Gamma_\gamma}{4(E - E_r)^2 + \Gamma^2} . \tag{75}$$

E_r is the energy separation between the levels, and σ_o is the maximum resonance cross section. It is given by

$$\sigma_o = \frac{2I_B + 1}{2I_A + 1} 2\pi \lambda\!\!\!^{-2} , \tag{76}$$

where the gamma ray of wavelength λ is emitted between the two states of spin I_B and I_A.

Despite the simplicity of this method, some difficulties exist. For lifetimes of the order of 10^{-10} second or longer extra-nuclear fields can widen the line, and one may find apparent lifetimes that are shorter than the real ones.[11]

Difficulties also arise for very short lifetimes. If the nuclear lifetime becomes comparable to, or shorter than, the inverse of the Debye frequency ($\sim 10^{-13}$ second), it is impossible to distinguish recoilless transitions from those in which the lattice takes up energy.

b. Nuclear Moments

The Mössbauer effect permits the determination of the nuclear moments (i. e., the spin, the magnetic dipole moment, and the electric quadrupole moment) in a direct way, provided certain conditions are met. For example, consider a nucleus with ground-state spin 0, and with the excited-state parameters spin I_B, magnetic moment μ_B, and g-factor g_B. If the nucleus is bound in a crystal so that the magnetic field and the electric field gradient are zero at the lattice site, then the emission and absorption lines will be unsplit.

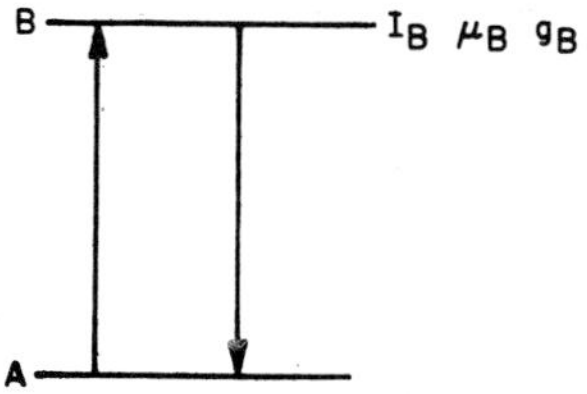

If an external magnetic field H is applied to the source or absorber the corresponding line will split into $2I_B + 1$ equally-spaced components, with a separation between the components of magnitude

$$\Delta = g_B \, \mu_o \, H, \tag{77}$$

where μ_o is the nuclear magneton. If the separation is larger than the width 2Γ of the overlap line, i. e., if

$$g_B \, \mu_o \, H \gtrsim 2\Gamma = \frac{2\hbar}{\tau} \, , \tag{78}$$

then the number of components can be counted and the spin I_B determined. From the splitting Δ, the nuclear g-factor g_B can also be determined if the strength of the external magnetic field is known. Knowing g_B and I_B, one can determine the magnetic moment of the excited state:

$$\mu_B = g_B \, \mu_o \, I_B. \tag{79}$$

173

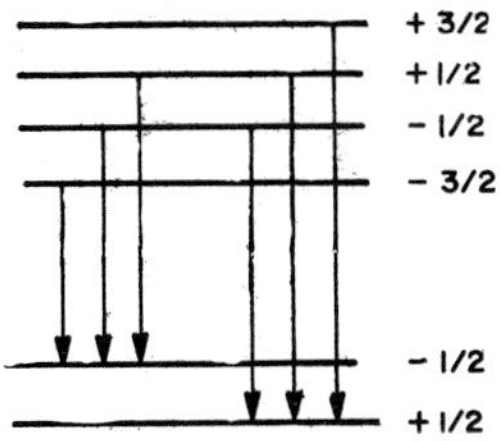

The strong internal magnetic fields in ferromagnets and paramagnetic substances are utilized in studying the nuclear Zeeman effect. This method is also very useful in determining the Curie temperature and Neel temperature of various compounds and solid solutions.

When there is an electric field gradient at the lattice site the nuclear quadrupole moment interacts with the field gradient. This quadrupole coupling is given by $\vec{Q} \cdot \vec{\nabla}\vec{E}$, where $\vec{Q}$ is the nuclear quadrupole moment and $\vec{\nabla}\vec{E}$ is the electric field gradient at the nuclear site. The emission or absorption line is split as shown in the diagram.

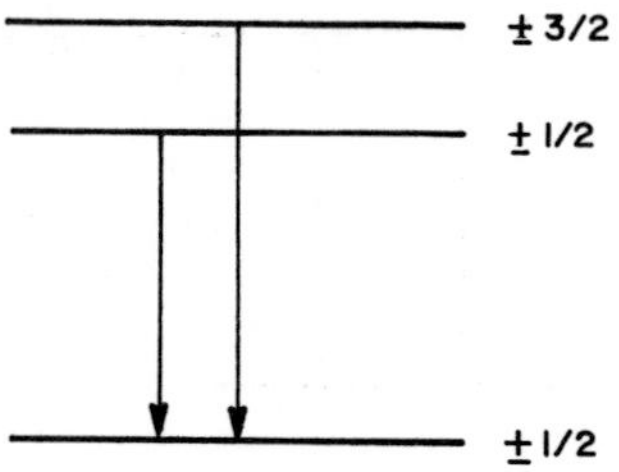

Fe^{57}

If the electric field gradient $\vec{\nabla}\vec{E}$ is calculated, then from the splitting the electric quadrupole moment $\vec{Q}$ can be found.

The electric field gradient (EFG) is evaluated by applying the gradient operation to the three components of the electric field, which is itself a vector. It is specified by the three components $\frac{\partial^2 V}{\partial x^2}$, $\frac{\partial^2 V}{\partial y^2}$, and $\frac{\partial^2 V}{\partial z^2}$, customarily written as V_{xx}, V_{yy}, and V_{zz}. These three components are not independent, as they must obey the Laplace equation in a region where the charge density vanishes:

$$V_{xx} + V_{yy} + V_{zz} = 0. \tag{80}$$

It might be noted here that the charge density of the s-electrons of the atoms at whose nuclear site the field gradient is being evaluated does not vanish; but because of the spherically symmetric distribution of the s-electrons, they do not contribute to the effect considered. Therefore, only two independent components are left, and they can be represented by V_{zz} and by the asymmetry parameter η:

$$\eta = \frac{V_{xx} - V_{yy}}{V_{zz}} . \tag{81}$$

V_{zz} is denoted by eq.

The interaction Hamiltonian between $\vec{Q}$ and the gradient of the electric field is

$$H = \vec{Q} \cdot \vec{\nabla} \vec{E} . \tag{82}$$

By means of the Wigner-Eckart theorem one may show that the expectation value of this interaction in the angular momentum state $|I\, m_I\rangle$ is

$$E_Q = \frac{e^2 q Q}{4I(2I-1)} \left[3m_I^2 - I(I+1)\right] \left(1 + \frac{\eta^2}{3}\right)^{1/2} , \tag{83}$$

$$m_I = I, I-1, \ldots, -I,$$

where $eQ \left(1 + \frac{\eta^2}{3}\right)^{1/2}$ is proportional to the reduced matrix element of the quadrupole moment operator. This expression contains only the second power of m_I; therefore, the states with the same values of m_I but of different signs remain degenerate.

If the crystal structure is known to high precision and if an ionic charge can be assigned to the lattice sites, then the value of the EFG at the atomic site can be obtained from a straightforward electrostatic calculation. However, this is not the EFG at the nuclear site. It is modified by the atom's own electrons, whose wave functions are distorted by interaction with the external EFG and as a result create an EFG of their own. This results in the amplification of the EFG due to the distant charges and is known as antishielding. This contribution can be denoted by $-\gamma_\infty$ eq, where $\gamma_\infty > 0$ represents a shielding factor. Therefore, Equation (83) is to be modified as

$$E_Q = \frac{e^2 q Q}{4I(2I-1)} \left(1 - \gamma_\infty\right) \left[3m_I^2 - I(I+1)\right] \left(1 + \frac{\eta^2}{3}\right)^{1/2} . \tag{84}$$

c. Isomeric Shift (Chemical Shift)

A change in the electrostatic interaction between the nucleus and its surrounding electrons produces corresponding shifts in energy of the atomic and nuclear levels. The same atomic transition can have a different energy in two atoms which contain nuclei in different states, provided the two atomic states involved in the transition are affected differently by the change in the nuclear radius; otherwise, both levels are shifted by the same amount, and there is no net change in the transition energy. In the nuclear isomer shift, the same nuclear transition in two atomic systems is compared which have different electronic wave functions at the nucleus. A shift can only be seen if the two nuclear states involved have different radii; otherwise, both levels involved in the transition change by the same amount, and the gamma ray energy is not affected. Therefore, the requirements for the observation of a nuclear isomeric shift are as follows:

1) The two nuclear states involved must have different charge distributions.
2) There must be electronic wave functions (usually from s-electrons) which overlap appreciably with the nuclear wave functions.
3) The wave functions must be sensitive to external chemical changes.

Let a finite-radius nucleus have a radius R_A in the ground state and a radius R_B in the excited state. Because of the overlap with the

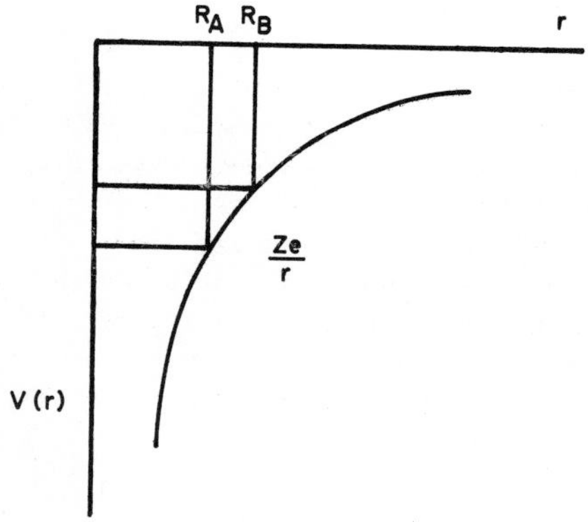

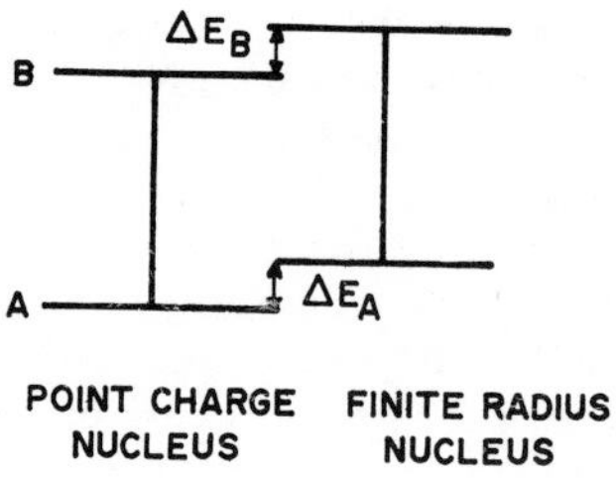

electronic wave functions, the two levels A and B will lie higher than for a point-charge nucleus. The potential from R_A to ∞ is not affected by the finite size of the nucleus when the state A is considered. Hence, only the volume from 0 to R_A needs to be considered in determining ΔE_A. Assume that the wave function $\Psi(r)$ of the relevant electrons is essentially constant over the distances involved and can be replaced by $\Psi(0)$. The contribution to the interaction energy from this volume is given by

$$E(R_A) = -\int_0^{R_A} V(r)\, e\, |\Psi(0)|^2\, 4\pi r^2 dr. \qquad (85)$$

For a point nucleus $V(r) = \frac{Ze}{r}$, so that

$$E^p\left(R_A\right) = -e\left|\Psi(o)\right|^2 \int_o^{R_A} \frac{Ze}{r} 4\pi r^2 \, dr$$

$$= -2\pi Ze^2 R_A^2 \left|\Psi(o)\right|^2 . \tag{86}$$

The energy $E\left(R_A\right)$ for a finite-size nucleus depends on the charge distribution. Let us consider a surface-charge model for the sake of simplicity. The electrostatic potential is constant from the center to the nuclear surface and joins the outside potential at r = R. The contribution of this potential to the interaction energy is given by

$$E^s\left(R_A\right) = -\frac{4}{3}\pi Ze^2 R_A^2 \left|\Psi(o)\right|^2 . \tag{87}$$

The difference between $E^s\left(R_A\right)$ and $E^p\left(R_A\right)$ yields the change in energy ΔE_A^s:

$$\Delta E_A^s = E^s\left(R_A\right) - E^p\left(R_A\right) = \frac{2}{3}\pi Ze^2 R_A^2 \left|\Psi(o)\right|^2 . \tag{88}$$

The assumption of a surface-charge model is unrealistic. Let us suppose instead that a uniform charge density ρ is distributed throughout the nucleus of radius R_A. Then the interaction energy, from Equation (85), can be written as

$$E_{R_A} = -e\int_o^{R_A} \left|\Psi(o)\right|^2 V \, 4\pi r^2 \, dr. \tag{89}$$

The potential V inside the sphere is

$$V = \frac{Ze}{R_A}\left[\frac{3}{2} - \frac{1}{2}\left(\frac{r}{R_A}\right)^2\right] . \tag{90}$$

Therefore,

$$E_{R_A} = -4\pi\left|\Psi(o)\right|^2 \frac{Ze^2}{R_A}\int_o^{R_A}\left[\frac{3}{2}-\frac{1}{2}\left(\frac{r}{R_A}\right)^2\right] r^2\,dr$$

$$= -2\pi\left|\Psi(o)\right|^2 Ze^2 R_A^2 + \frac{2\pi}{5}\left|\Psi(o)\right|^2 Ze^2 R_A^2$$

$$= -2\pi Ze^2 R_A^2\left|\Psi(o)\right|^2 + \frac{2\pi}{5} Ze^2 R_A^2\left|\Psi(o)\right|^2 . \quad (91)$$

The difference between E_{R_A} and $E^p_{R_A}$ is given by

$$\Delta E_A = \frac{2\pi}{5} Ze^2 R_A^2\left|\Psi(o)\right|^2 . \quad (92)$$

Therefore, the transition energy between the levels B and A is

$$E_o' = E_o + \Delta E_B - \Delta E_A$$

$$= E_o + \frac{2\pi}{5} Ze^2 \left|\Psi(o)\right|^2\left[R_B^2 - R_A^2\right] \quad (93)$$

The energy shift given by Equation (93) is vanishingly small for the changes in $\left|\Psi(o)\right|^2$ normally encountered. However, this small change can be measured in the Mössbauer effect experiments, because the nuclear transition in a source is compared with that in an absorber. The isomeric shift, which is the difference in energy between the source and the absorber, can be written as

$$I.S. = \frac{2\pi}{5} Ze^2\left(R_B^2 - R_A^2\right)\left\{\left|\Psi(o)\right|^2_{absorb} - \left|\Psi(o)\right|^2_{source}\right\} \quad (94)$$

If the substitutions $R_B = R_e$, the nuclear radius at the excited state, and $R_A = R_g$, the nuclear radius at the ground state of the nucleus are made, Equation (94) can be modified into

$$I.S. = \frac{2\pi}{5} Ze^2\left(R_e^2 - R_g^2\right)\left\{\left|\Psi(o)\right|^2_{absorb} - \left|\Psi(o)\right|^2_{source}\right\}, \quad (95)$$

or

$$I.S. = \frac{4\pi}{5} Ze^2 R_g^2\left(\frac{\delta R}{R_g}\right)\left\{\left|\Psi(o)\right|^2_{absorb} - \left|\Psi(o)\right|^2_{source}\right\}. \quad (96)$$

In this last expression we have put $R_e + R_g \approx 2 R_g$, $\delta R = R_e - R_g$, and $R_g = r_0 A^{1/3}$, where $r_0 = 1.2 \times 10^{-13}$ cm and A is the number of nucleons in the nucleus. Equations (95) and (96) consist of two factors, of which $\{|\Psi(o)|^2_{absorb} - |\Psi(o)|^2_{source}\}$ is basically an atomic or chemical parameter (since $|\Psi(o)|^2_{absorb}$ and $|\Psi(o)|^2_{source}$ are the total s-electron densities at the nucleus for absorber and emitter, respectively). The other factor $(R_e^2 - R_g^2)$ is nuclear in its origin.

An examination of the Hartree-Fock calculations[12] shows that there are significant differences in the value of $|\Psi_{3s}(o)|^2$ for different 3d-configurations in iron; the change in $|\Psi_{1s}(o)|^2$ and $|\Psi_{2s}(o)|^2$ is substantially smaller. The variation in $|\Psi_{3s}(o)|^2$ corresponds to different degrees of shielding of 3s by 3d-electrons. Therefore, a sizable isomeric shift is observed by the use of ionic Fe^{2+} and Fe^{3+} salts (the latter being obtained by the removal of the sixth 3d-electron from divalent iron). If we make the assumption that the electronic charge density in an ionic salt is the same as in a free ion, then the results of Hartree-Fock calculations, where these are available, can be used to evaluate the chemical factor in Equation (96). The experimental values of isomeric shifts then allow a determination of the change of the nuclear radius $\frac{(\delta R)}{R}$ between the excited state and the ground state. This information is vital in the theory of nuclear models.

10. Optical Analogues of the Mössbauer Effect in Solids

From the classical theory of the Mössbauer effect, we have already seen that if we have a gamma ray of frequency ω_0 emitted by a nucleus which is itself in motion with a velocity v, then the instantaneous frequency as seen by an observer at rest will vary with time. We can write

$$\omega_n\left(\vec{x}, t\right) = \omega_0 + \omega_0 v\left(\vec{x}, t\right) c^{-1} + \frac{1}{2} \omega_0 v^2\left(\vec{x}, t\right) c^{-2} + \dots \tag{97}$$

If the motion of the host crystal is described by the function $\mu\left(\vec{x}, t\right)$ giving the displacement from equilibrium at time t of the atom at position $\vec{x}$, then the velocity of the atom is $\dot{\mu}\left(\vec{x}, t\right)$ and we have

$$\omega_n\left(\vec{x}, t\right) = \omega_0 \left[1 + c^{-1} \dot{\mu}\left(\vec{x}, t\right) + \frac{1}{2} c^{-2} \dot{\mu}^2\left(\vec{x}, t\right) + \dots\right] . \tag{98}$$

We have already demonstrated that the resulting spectrum will be a central peak corresponding to recoilless emission with a continuous spectrum on either side of the line. These continuous spectra extend over a range of frequencies comparable with or larger than the typical frequencies describing the time variation of the displacement function $\mu(\vec{x}, t)$. The detailed shape of this broad structure depends on the time-dependence of $\mu(\vec{x}, t)$, while the intensity increases as the mean amplitude of motion of the emitting nucleus increases. This structure is, of course, the multiphonon structure of the gamma ray spectrum.

A closely similar picture describes the emission of light when an electron makes a transition between states of an ion or a structural defect in a crystal.[13,14] In the electronic case, the transition energy is strongly influenced by the positions of the atoms or ions near the excited ion or defect; and the important coupling to the motion in the crystal is through the relative displacements of the neighboring atoms, not through the velocity of the emitting ion. The formalism remains the same, however, as a result of the invariance of the energy $\frac{1}{2}(p^2 + q^2)$ of the oscillator with respect to the replacement of the momentum by the coordinate. There is, of course, a Doppler coupling to the lattice motion, but this is typically very small compared to the strain coupling. Let us assume a continuum model and let the energy shift be simply a function of the local strain $\epsilon(x, t)$ at the defect. This strain may be written as the gradient of the displacement function; therefore,

$$\omega_e(\vec{x}, t) = \omega_0 + \alpha\epsilon(\vec{x}, t) + \beta\epsilon^2(\vec{x}, t) + \ldots$$

$$= \omega_0 + \alpha\vec{\nabla}\mu(\vec{x}, t) + \beta\left[\vec{\nabla}\mu(\vec{x}, t)\right]^2 + \cdots . \qquad (99)$$

Equations (98) and (99) are essentially the same, except that the time derivative in Equation (98) has been replaced by a space derivative in Equation (99). The frequency spectra will then be similar, and one expects to see a close parallel between the two types of systems.

In an approximation the formal analogy may be extended by expressing the displacement function $\mu(x, t)$ in terms of phonon coordinates. The frequency dependence of the coupling to the phonons is the same for both the problems. This is strictly valid for phonons at long wavelength, and also gives reasonable values for the coupling to short-wavelength phonons for localized defects, but it is not appropriate for defects (such as impurities in semiconductors) which have electron orbits that are large compared with the lattice parameter.

We can further compare the nuclear and optical processes in the following way. After the emission of a gamma-ray photon, the emitting nucleus has a momentum in excess of its typical zero-point momentum and a kinetic energy of recoil associated with this momentum recoil. Classically, one would expect this recoil kinetic energy to be dissipated as heat in the crystal; but as we have seen earlier, there is a nonvanishing probability that the system will be in its ground vibrational state after the emission. This probability is appreciable if the recoil momentum is comparable to, or small compared to, the zero-point momentum of the nucleus.

Similarly, after the emission of the optical photon the nuclei near the electron are displaced from their new equilibrium positions, or have a "displacement recoil"; and associated with this displacement is a potential energy of recoil. Classically, one would expect this recoil potential energy to be dissipated as heat in the crystal; but quantum-mechanically there is a nonvanishing probability that the system will be in its ground vibrational state after the emission. This probability will be appreciable if the recoil displacement is comparable to or small compared with the zero-point displacement of the nuclei.

The analogy may be expressed in still a different way. If the crystal is considered to be a giant molecule and the gamma ray or optical spectrum is described in the language of band spectra, the Mössbauer line and its optical analogue, when observed at T = 0°K, are zero-zero transitions of the band spectrum. In the solid, all higher order bands or lines typically merge into a continuum, and the spectrum is characterized in both nuclear and electronic systems by a sharp zero-zero transition and a continuous single and multiphonon spectrum.

In the study of lattice dynamics and vibrational modes, the application of the Mössbauer effect has certain disadvantages. First, very high source velocities are required to obtain a sufficient Doppler shift to scan the frequency range of interest. Second, the method suffers from the requirement of an excessively high resolution, and the search for a localized mode becomes exceedingly difficult if there is an appreciable lifetime broadening of the localized mode. Thus, the optical technique is much more feasible experimentally for the study of normal and local vibrational modes.

LITERATURE CITED

1. R. L. Mössbauer, KERNRESONANZFLUORESZENZ von GAMMASTRAHLUNG IN Ir^{191}, Zeitschrift für Physik, Vol. 151, 1958, pp. 124-143.

2. R. L. Mössbauer, KERNRESONANZFLUORESZENZ von GAMMASTRAHLUNG IN Ir^{191}, Die Naturwissenschaften, Vol. 45, 1958, pp. 538, 539.

3. H. Frauenfelder, THE MÖSSBAUER EFFECT, New York, W. A. Benjamin, Incorporated, 1963.

4. P. B. Moon, RESONANT NUCLEAR SCATTERING OF GAMMA-RAYS: THEORY AND PRELIMINARY EXPERIMENTS, The Proceedings of the Physical Society (London), Vol. 64, 1951, pp. 76-82.

5. F. R. Metzger, RESONANCE FLUORESCENCE IN NUCLEI, Progress In Nuclear Physics, Vol. 7, 1959, pp. 54-88.

6. V. F. Weisskopf, SELECTED TOPICS IN THEORETICAL PHYSICS, Lectures In Theoretical Physics, New York, Interscience Publishers Incorporated, London, Interscience Publishers Ltd., 1960, pp. 54-105, (Editors - Wesley E. Brittin, B. W. Downs, and Joanne Downs).

7. H. J. Lipkin, SOME SIMPLE FEATURES OF THE MÖSSBAUER EFFECT, Annals of Physics, Vol. 9, 1960, pp. 332-339.

8. R. L. Mössbauer, LES PRIX NOBEL EN 1961, Nobel Foundation, Stockholm, 1962 (Translation in Science, Vol. 137, 1962, p. 731).

9. F. L. Shapiro, THE MÖSSBAUER EFFECT, Uspekhi Fizicheskikh Nauk, Vol. 72, December 1960, pp. 685-696, English Translation in Soviet Physics Uspekhi, Vol. 4, No. 6, May-June 1961, pp. 881-887.

10. W. E. Lamb, Jr., CAPTURE OF NEUTRONS BY ATOMS IN A CRYSTAL, Physical Review, Vol. 55, 1939, pp. 190-197.

11. R. L. Mössbauer, RECOILLESS NUCLEAR RESONANCE ABSORPTION, Annual Review of Nuclear Science, Vol. 12, 1962, p. 123.

12. Solid State and Molecular Theory Group, Massachusetts Institute of Technology, Cambridge, Massachusetts, IRON SERIES HARTREE-FOCK CALCULATIONS by R. E. Watson, 15 June 1959, Technical Report No. 12 (Unpublished) (Unclassified Report).

13. E. D. Trifonov, THE PROBABILITY OF PHONON FREE TRANSITION AT THE IMPURITY CENTERS OF CRYSTALS, Doklady Akademii Nauk, SSSR, Vol. 147, 1963, p. 826, English Translation in Soviet Physics-Doklady, Vol. 7, June 1963, pp. 1105-1107.

14. R. H. Silsbee and D. B. Fitchen, OPTICAL ANALOGS OF THE MÖSSBAUER EFFECT IN SOLIDS, Reviews of Modern Physics, Vol. 36, 1964, pp. 432-436.

QUANTUM FIELD THEORY OF LATTICE VIBRATIONS IN THE HARMONIC APPROXIMATION

by

ROMAS A. SHATAS,

C. ALTON COULTER, JOHN D. STETTLER,

and DAVID W. HOWGATE

Solid State Physics Branch
Physical Sciences Laboratory
Research and Development Directorate
U. S. Army Missile Command
Redstone Arsenal, Alabama 35809

ABSTRACT. We develop the concept of the quasiparticle of the free lattice vibrational field in the formalism of quantum field theory. First we review the procedure of first-quantization of the lattice in the harmonic approximation. The classical Hamiltonian of a lattice is describable by a sum of Hamiltonians, each characterizing a member of a set of harmonic oscillators. Any oscillator of this set can be first-quantized by the procedure $H \sim \frac{1}{2}(p^2 + q^2) \rightarrow \hbar(cc^+ + c^+c)$, $[c_i, c_j^+]_- = \delta_{ij}$. This leads to the occupation number representation $H \sim \hbar(N + \frac{1}{2})$, with N, the number operator, given by the bilinear form $c^+c = N$. Here $c^+ \sim (p + iq)$ and its adjoint, c, are raising and lowering operators of the energy eigenstates of one vibrational mode. The c's, although they obey the same commutation relations as creation and annihilation operators, are only first-quantized. This is seen from the following facts: (1) the c's are given by a linear combination of the non-commuting dynamical variables p and q, which themselves are first-quantized either in the coordinate or the momentum representation. Therefore, the number operator in the occupation number representation is also only first-quantized; (2) the operation $c^+ |0\rangle$, where $|0\rangle$ designates a physical vacuum state, is not meaningful for any set of c's. However, in a second-quantized theory proper, a creation operator operating on the vacuum state creates a one-particle state. Consequently, we employ a second-quantization procedure in which the wave functions of the first quantized harmonic oscillator problem in the coordinate representation are replaced by field operators Ψ^+, Ψ. Their expansion in an orthonormal set of functions satisfying the differential equation of the harmonic oscillator in the coordinate representation yields a set of operator expansion coefficients b_n^+, b_n which are the creation and annihilation operators of the second-quantized formalism. The consistency of our results is shown by demonstrating the equivalence of the first-and second-quantized lattice Hamiltonians. The creation operators of the second-quantized problem have the property that the operation $b_n^+|0\rangle$ (where $|0\rangle$ defines a physical vacuum state with no lattice vibrational modes present) exists and creates a lattice quasiparticle occupying the n-th state of a vibrational mode having a discrete spectrum of eigenstates of equal energy separation. Therefore, b_n^+ is called a phonon mode creation

*Permanent address: Department of Physics, Clark University, Worcester, Massachusetts.

operator and its adjoint, b_n, a phonon mode annihilation operator. Since for the lattice only one occupied state per vibrational mode is meaningful, the number of lattice quasiparticles is identical with the number of lattice vibrational modes. With this one-particle-per-mode requirement, the conventional phonon raising and lowering operators can be expressed as a bilinear combination of the vibrational mode creation and annihilation operators. Since the number of lattice vibrational modes is a constant for a given lattice, the number of the new lattice quasiparticles is therefore a constant motion, a property with significant advantages in many applications in solid state physics.

CONTENTS

1. INTRODUCTION. Quantization of the classical electromagnetic field describable by Maxwell's equations has led to the concept of photons. Their reality has been demonstrated many times since Albert Einstein explained the photo-electric effect by postulating $E = h\nu$. Some twenty years later Igor Tamm proposed, in analogy to the quasiparticle of the radiation field, the name phonon for the quasiparticle resulting from the quantization of lattice vibrations. The general validity of the phonon concept has been proven in many experiments in which vibrational states of the lattice are involved [1].

In the mathematical description of this phonon concept it has been customary to employ a set of phonon "raising and lowering operators" constructed from a linear combination of the position and momentum operators of the harmonic oscillators which represent the lattice in phonon space. This representation of the lattice as a collection of harmonic oscillators and the introduction of the raising and lowering operators are, for completeness, reviewed in Sections 2 and 3. Since it happens that the raising and lowering operators which appear in this formulation of the theory satisfy the same commutation relations as the creation and annihilation operators of quantum field theory, the formulation has conventionally been considered as a second-quantized theory in which the raising and lowering operators play the roles of creation and annihilation operators. However, if this interpretation of the theory is adopted one finds that when the lattice interacts with some other system (such as an electron trapped in a lattice defect) then the number of lattice quasiparticles "created" by these operators is not a constant of the motion; that is, the conventional phonon number operator does not commute with the Hamiltonian. This non-commutation sometimes causes difficulties in applications of the theory.

These difficulties may be circumvented by using a field-theoretical ("second-quantized") formulation of the problem. Formall the transition to this representation of the theory is carried out by appropriately replacing wavefunctions by operator fields in the first-quantized version of the theory [2] , [3] . In Section 4 this second-quantization procedure is applied to the harmonic oscillators representative of the lattice in phonon space, with an operator field being introduced for each vibrational coordinate, and a new lattice quasiparticle concept for the vibrational field of a crystalline lattice is worked out. In this formalism there is a one-to-one correspondence between lattice quasiparticles and vibrational modes of the lattice. The new quasiparticles therefore constitute a canonical ensemble, rather than a grand canonical ensemble as in the case of the conventional phonons [4] . They can be created directly from the physical vacuum state by applying a phonon mode creation operator, again in contrast with the conventional formalism. The construction of a Hamiltonian for an interacting system in which the operator for the total number of the new lattice quasiparticles commutes with the Hamiltonian even in the interacting case is dealt with in Section 5.

2. Linear Monatomic Harmonic Lattice in Phonon Space

We write the Lagrangian function for a discrete linear monatomic lattice in the harmonic approximation, with mass and spring constant equal to unity, as follows:

$$L = \frac{1}{2} \sum_i \dot{q}_i^2 - \frac{1}{2} \sum_i (q_{i+1} - q_i)^2 \quad . \tag{1}$$

The corresponding Hamiltonian function is then obtained by applying the transformation relation

$$H = \sum_i p_i \dot{q}_i - L, \quad p_i = \frac{\partial L}{\partial \dot{q}_i} = \dot{q}_i$$

(2)

$$H = \frac{1}{2} \sum_i [p_i^2 + (q_{i+1} - q_i)^2] \quad .$$

The usual way of obtaining an operator expression for the above Hamiltonian is to establish the analogy with an ensemble of harmonic oscillators. To obtain an equivalent set of harmonic oscillators representing the discrete lattice we use the property of periodicity of the lattice and expand the direct lattice space coordinate q_i (with conjugate momentum p_i) in phonon space coordinates Q_k (conjugate momentum P_k), also often referred to as normal coordinates and momenta. Accordingly, the vibrational modes of the lattice in the phonon space are called the normal modes. We choose an N-dimensional Hilbert space spanned by orthogonal trigonometric functions as the carrier space for phonons, and accomplish the transformation between the direct and the phonon space by the complex Fourier series given by

(3) $$p_r = \frac{1}{\sqrt{N}} \sum_k P_k e^{-ikr} , \quad q_r = \frac{1}{\sqrt{N}} \sum_k Q_k e^{ikr} .$$

Using periodic boundary conditions for the lattice of N elements (N odd) that $q_{n+N} = q_n$, $-(N-1)/2 \leq n \leq +(N-1)/2$, one finds that $e^{ikN} = 1$ and $k = 2\pi n/N$. We then obtain the orthogonality and normalization condition

(4) $$\sum_k e^{ik(r-s)} = N\delta(r,s) ,$$

and write the expansion of the normal coordinate Q_k and momentum P_k as follows:

(5) $$P_k = \frac{1}{\sqrt{N}} \sum_s p_s e^{iks} , \quad Q_k = \frac{1}{\sqrt{N}} \sum_s q_s e^{-iks} .$$

Since q, p are defined in direct lattice space and are observable, we require that they be Hermitian. Taking the Hermitian adjoint of Eq. (3), we find that $Q_k = Q^+_{-k}$ and similarly that $P_k = P^+_{-k}$. This non-Hermiticity of the normal coordinate and its conjugate momentum is merely due to our choice of the expansion function e^{ikr}. If the sine and cosine form of the Fourier series is used, both Q_k and P_k are Hermitian. However, for analytical purposes the complex Fourier series is much more convenient, and we will restore the Hermiticity later. Within this choice of the expansion the coordinate of the direct lattice q_r is transparently Hermitian if Eq. (3) is symmetrized by writing

(6) $$q_r = \frac{1}{2} \frac{1}{\sqrt{N}} \sum_k (Q_k e^{ikr} + Q_k^+ e^{-ikr}) .$$

By taking the adjoint of Eq. (6), one sees easily that $q_r = q_r^+$.

To obtain the Langrangian and the Hamiltonian functions in phonon space, we calculate the square of Eq. (3) and use the normalization and orthogonality relation Eq. (5) to obtain the expression

$$\sum_r (\dot{q}_r)^2 = \sum_k \dot{Q}_k \dot{Q}_{-k} .$$

In writing the right side of this expression we have made use of the fact that k extends over positive as well as negative numbers. By a similar procedure we obtain the potential energy term as $\sum_k (1 - \cos k) Q_k Q_{-k}$. Thus, the Lagrangian function in the phonon space assumes the following form:

$$L = \tfrac{1}{2} \sum_k \dot{Q}_k \dot{Q}_{-k} - \sum_k (1 - \cos k) Q_k Q_{-k} . \tag{7}$$

By applying the usual procedures, we obtain the Hamiltonian function in phonon space:

$$H = \tfrac{1}{2} \sum_k P_k P_{-k} + \sum_k (1 - \cos k) Q_k Q_{-k} . \tag{8}$$

3. Quantization of the Free Phonon Hamiltonian in the Formalism of Harmonic Oscillator Ladder Operators

It is easy to verify that the normal coordinates and momenta of Eq. (8) obey the equal time commutation relation for canonically-conjugate variables; e.g.,

$$[Q_k , P_{k'}]_- = i\hbar \delta_{k,k'} \tag{9}$$

if

$$[q_r , p_{r'}]_- = i\hbar \delta_{r,r'} .$$

At this point, let us recall that an observable having a physically measurable expectation value must be representable by a Hermitian operator in quantum theory. Therefore, we want to demonstrate that by employing a simple algebraic procedure we may express the P's and Q's in real phonon space. Following Maradudin, Montroll, and Weiss [5], we may transform to standing wave amplitudes ${}^cQ_k$ and ${}^sQ_k$ by taking the following linear combination:

(5a)

$$Q_o = \sqrt{2}\ {}^cQ_o, \quad {}^sQ_o = 0, \; k = 0 ,$$

$$Q_k = \frac{1}{\sqrt{2}}\,[\,{}^cQ_k + i\,{}^sQ_k] \;, \quad Q_{-k} = \frac{1}{\sqrt{2}}\,[\,{}^cQ_k - i\,{}^sQ_k] \;, \; k \neq 0 \;.$$

Although the ${}^cQ_k$ and ${}^sQ_k$ are real, the Q_k are complex and satisfy the adjoint relation $Q_k^+ = Q_{-k}$ shown earlier. Within this choice of normal coordinates and momenta, the direct lattice coordinate expansion given earlier by Eq. (6) assumes the form

(6a)

$$q_r = \sqrt{\frac{2}{N}} \sum_{k>o} ({}^cQ_k \cos kr - {}^sQ_k \sin kr) \;.$$

Here the summation is restricted to only nonnegative k values, $k = (2\pi/N)n$, $0 \leq n \leq N$. Actually, the $k = 0$ term corresponds to the "translational mode," and has been omitted from consideration since vibrational modes only are being discussed. In the future, we shall confine our attention to the case $k \neq 0$.

Finally, it can be seen that should we desire traveling waves, we can relate the complex normal coordinates and momenta (Q_k, P_k) to a real set $({}^rQ_k \,, {}^rP_{-k})$ by the transformation

(5b)

$$Q_k = \frac{1}{2}\,[\,{}^rQ_{-k} + {}^rQ_k] + i/2\,[2(1 - \cos k)]^{-\frac{1}{2}}\,[\,{}^rP_k - {}^rP_{-k}] \;,$$

$$P_k = \frac{1}{2}\,[\,{}^rP_{-k} + {}^rP_k] + i/2\,[2(1 - \cos k)]^{\frac{1}{2}}\,[\,{}^rQ_k - {}^rQ_{-k}] \;.$$

Thus, normal coordinates and momenta defined in the phonon space can be easily made Hermitian; and therefore the equivalent set of harmonic oscillators is not a mere mental abstraction such as, for example, is constructed to represent an electromagnetic field. (Needless to say, one would need to resuscitate the ether hypothesis in order to attach a direct significance to the p's and q's of an ensemble of harmonic oscillators representing the electromagnetic field.)

The classical Hamiltonian function for a harmonic oscillator with mass and spring constant equal to unity has the form

$$H = \frac{1}{2}(p^2 + q^2) .$$

The equivalent quantum-mechanical expression is conveniently written in terms of raising and lowering operators c^+ and c, respectively, defined as a linear combination of p and q:

$$c = \frac{1}{\sqrt{2\hbar}}(p - iq)$$

(10)

$$c+ = \frac{1}{\sqrt{2\hbar}}(p + iq) \quad .$$

Use of Eq. (10) in the harmonic oscillator Hamiltonian yields a symmetric combination, bilinear in the c's, of the form

$$H = H^+ = \frac{\hbar}{2}(c c^+ + c^+ c) \quad .$$

This is easily modified by the relation $[c, c^+]_- = 1$ to read $H = \hbar(c^+c + \frac{1}{2}$ The bilinear combination c^+c is called the number operator, and therefore this representation of the harmonic oscillator is referred to as the occupation number representation. In Heisenberg matrix mechanics, the ladder operators c and c^+ are represented by the following non-diagonal matrices:

(10a) $$c = \begin{vmatrix} 0 & \sqrt{1} & 0 & 0 & . \\ 0 & 0 & \sqrt{2} & 0 & . \\ 0 & 0 & 0 & \sqrt{3} & . \\ . & . & . & . & . \end{vmatrix}$$

(10b) $$c^+ = \begin{vmatrix} 0 & 0 & 0 & 0 & . \\ \sqrt{1} & 0 & 0 & 0 & . \\ 0 & \sqrt{2} & 0 & 0 & . \\ 0 & 0 & \sqrt{3} & 0 & . \\ . & . & . & . & . \end{vmatrix}$$

It is seen immediately that the number operator N is represented by a diagonal matrix having the form

$$N = \begin{vmatrix} 0 & 0 & 0 & . \\ 0 & 1 & 0 & . \\ 0 & 0 & 2 & . \\ . & . & . & . \end{vmatrix} .$$

In this connection, we note that the operation $c^+ |0\rangle' = |1\rangle$, e.g., the raising operator operating on the ground state of the harmonic oscillator, is defined only for

$$|0\rangle' = \begin{vmatrix} 1 \\ 0 \\ 0 \\ . \\ . \\ . \end{vmatrix} .$$

This is not the physical vacuum state.

We employ a completely analogous precedure to obtain the occupation number representation for the equivalent oscillators of the lattice having an arbitrary mass and spring constant. First, we define a set of raising and lowering operators of the k-th vibrational mode c_k^+ and c_k, respectively, by the following expressions:

(11)
$$c_k = \frac{1}{\sqrt{2\hbar\,\omega_k\, m}} (P_{-k} - i\, m\omega_k\, Q_k) ,$$
$$c_k^+ = \frac{1}{\sqrt{2\hbar\,\omega_k\, m}} (P_k + i\, m\omega_k\, Q_{-k}) ,$$

(12)
$$c_{-k} = \frac{1}{\sqrt{2\hbar\,\omega_k\, m}} (P_k - i\, m\omega_k\, Q_{-k}) ,$$
$$c_{-k}^+ = \frac{1}{\sqrt{2\hbar\,\omega_k\, m}} (P_{-k} + i\, m\omega_k\, Q_k) .$$

By an algebraic manipulation of the c_k's, we obtain the following equalitie which express the normal coordinates and their conjugate momenta in terms of the raising and lowering operators :

(13)

$$P_k = \sqrt{\frac{\hbar \omega_k m}{2}} \quad (c_k^+ + c_{-k}) ,$$

$$P_{-k} = \sqrt{\frac{\hbar \omega_k m}{2}} \quad (c_k + c_{-k}^+) ,$$

(14)

$$Q_k = -i\sqrt{\frac{\hbar}{2\omega_k m}} \quad (c_{-k}^+ - c_k) ,$$

$$Q_{-k} = +i \sqrt{\frac{\hbar}{2\omega_k m}} (c_{-k} - c_k^+) .$$

It is easy to see that the operators P_k, P_{-k}, Q_k and Q_{-k} are non-Hermiti in the same sense as their classical counterparts defined in Eqs. (3) and (5). However, q and p expressed as complex Fourier series in the norma coordinates and momenta Q_k and P_k, respectively, can be made Hermitia as seen in (6). Again, this merely reflects the choice of our expansion in normal modes taken to be consistent with often-used reference sources [6]. Obviously we could have employed Eq. (5a) or (5b) to formulate the same problem for real normal coordinates and momenta without affecting the physical content of the theory. The Hamiltonian for the equivalent set of phonon oscillators expressed in terms of the c's is written as a linear combination of operators for every vibrational mode k, each mode being represented by one oscillator:

(15)

$$H = \sum_k H_k = \frac{1}{2} \sum_k \hbar \omega_k (c_k^+ c_k + c_{-k} c_{-k}^+) .$$

We will now proceed to prove that the Hamiltonian Eq. (15) is equival to the classical expression Eq. (8). By inserting the c_k's defined by Eqs. (11) and (12), we get

$$H = \frac{1}{2m} \sum_k \{P_k P_{-k} + \omega_k^2 m^2 Q_k Q_{-k}\} ,$$

where we obtained the last expression by recalling that the vibrational mode index k is symmetric in its positive and negative values. By setting

(16) $$\omega_k^2 = 2(1 - \cos k), \qquad m = 1 ,$$

we display the equivalence of the two Hamiltonians. A further simplification of the Hamiltonian (15) can be obtained by noting that the phonon ladder operators obey the commutation relations

(17) $$[c_{\underline{+}k} , c^+_{\underline{+}k'}]_- = \delta_{kk'} .$$

(Eq. (17) is easily proved by using Eqs. (11) and (12) to replace the c_k's and by evaluating the Q, P commutator brackets by means of Eq. (9) and the auxiliary commutators $[Q_{\underline{+}k} , Q_{\overline{+}k}]_- = 0$, $[P_{\underline{+}k} , P_{\overline{+}k}]_- = 0$.) With the help of Eq. (17), the free phonon Hamiltonian is written as follows:

(18) $$H = \sum_k \hbar\omega_k (c_k^+ c_k + \tfrac{1}{2}) = \sum_k \hbar\omega_k (N_k + \tfrac{1}{2}) ,$$

where $c_k^+ c_k = N_k$ is the occupation number operator of the equivalent k-th harmonic oscillator. The lattice coordinate in direct lattice space given by Eq. (6) is expressed in quantized form by using Eq. (14):

(19) $$q_r = -i \sum_k \sqrt{\frac{\hbar}{2N\omega_k m}} \, (c_k^+ e^{-ikr} - c_k e^{ikr}) .$$

By taking the adjoint of Eq. (19), we ascertain that the quantized q_r is a Hermitian operator.

It is of importance to recall that in this discussion the raising and lowering operators c_k^+ , c_k were constructed from a linear combination of Q_k and P_k, the canonically-conjugate variables of the equivalent harmonic oscillator of the k-th vibrational mode. In the procedure known as first quantization, we replace the variable P_k by the operator $- i\hbar \frac{\partial}{\partial Q_k}$ if we choose the coordinate representation [7]. With equal ease we can also employ the momentum representation in which case we substitute $i\hbar \frac{\partial}{\partial P_k}$

for the variable Q_k. It has been emphasized earlier that the operation $c_k^+ |0\rangle$, where $|0\rangle$ designates the physical vacuum state, is not definable for our phonon raising operators. However, a creation operato in a quantum field theory actually creates a particle from the physical vacuum state, a property which our raising operators c_k^+ certainly do nc possess. In fact, our phonon raising and lowering operators are merely harmonic oscillator ladder operators which raise or lower energy eigen-states of an already-existing vibrational mode associated with a harmonic oscillator in phonon space. The failure of many authors to make this distinction has led to a misconception as to the origin and significance of the conventional phonon raising and lowering operators. An alternate formulation of the theory for the free phonon field with these objections removed is given in the next section.

4. The Second-Quantized Free Phonon Hamiltonian

We now wish to obtain the field-theoretical or second-quantized form of the theory for a harmonic lattice, in which the physical system is described by a coordinate-dependent operator field. The first-quantized Hamiltonian for a general three-dimensional harmonic lattice can be written in the form

$$\mathcal{H} = \sum_s \frac{\vec{P}_s^2}{2M_s} + \sum_{s,s'} \sum_{\alpha,\beta=1}^{3} A_{\alpha\beta}^{ss'} Q_\alpha^s Q_\beta^{s'} , \tag{20}$$

where $\vec{Q}^s$ (with components Q_α^s) is the displacement of the s-th ion, M_s is its mass, and P_s is its momentum. The $A_{\alpha\beta}^{ss'}$ are a set of constants characteristic of the lattice. The symbol $\mathcal{H}$ has been used here for the <u>first</u>-quantized Hamiltonian so that we may reserve the H for the second-quantized Hamiltonian which will be introduced shortly. As is well knowr it is possible to introduce a new set of coordinates q_k which are linearly related to the Q_α^s and which diagonalize (20); in terms of the q_k and their conjugate momenta p_k, the Hamiltonian $\mathcal{H}$ takes the form

$$\mathcal{H} = \sum_k \left(\frac{p_k^2}{2m_k} + \tfrac{1}{2} m_k \omega_k^2 q_k^2 \right) . \tag{20a}$$

This result is entirely similar to that obtained for the one-dimensional monatomic lattice considered earlier. In the general case considered he: however, it is not possible to give simple explicit expressions for the masses m_k and frequencies ω_k.

In order to obtain the appropriate second-quantized Hamiltonian corresponding to (20a), it is important to remember that it is customary to think of each vibrational coordinate q_k as characterizing a degree of freedom of the system which is distinct from the other degrees of freedom in the same sense that two types of particles with different physical properties are distinct from one another. This means that in the second-quantized form of the theory characterized by $\mathcal{H}$ it is necessary to introduce an operator field $\phi_k(q_k)$ for each index k. To find the explicit form of the second-quantized Hamiltonian containing the ϕ_k, we can use the following standard prescription: in the expression for the expectation value of the first-quantized Hamiltonian $\mathcal{H}$ (p, q) in the state of the system determined by the wave function.

$$\Phi(q) = \prod_k \Phi_k(q_k) ,$$

replace each $\Phi_k(q_k)$ by the operator field $\phi_k(q_k)$, and Φ_k^* by ϕ_k^+. Since

$$\langle \mathcal{H} \rangle = \sum_k \int \Phi_k^*(q_k) \cdot \left[-\frac{\hbar^2}{2m_k} \frac{d^2}{dq_k^2} + \tfrac{1}{2} m_k \omega_k^2 q_k^2 \right] \Phi_k(q_k) dq_k ,$$

we obtain for the second-quantized Hamiltonian

$$H = \sum_k \int \phi_k^+(q_k) \cdot \left[-\frac{\hbar^2}{2m_k} \frac{d^2}{dq_k^2} + \tfrac{1}{2} m_k \omega_k^2 q_k^2 \right] \phi_k(q_k) dq_k . \tag{21}$$

To complete the specification of the theory we now require that

(22)

$$\left[\phi_k(q_k) , \phi_j(q_j') \right]_- = 0 ,$$

$$\left[\phi_k(q_k) , \phi_j^+(q_j') \right]_- = \delta_{kj} \, \delta(q_k - q_j') ,$$

and that the time dependence of the ϕ_k (which has not been explicitly indicated) be determined by the usual Heisenberg equations of motion. (It would be possible to use anticommutation rather than commutation relations in (22) without altering any of the subsequent results.)

It is possible to write (21) in a form which makes its physical interpretation more transparent. Since H is a sum of independent, commuting terms, let us consider a typical one of these and write

$$(23) \qquad H = \int \phi^{+}(q) \left[-\frac{\hbar^2}{2m\omega}\frac{d^2}{dq^2} + \tfrac{1}{2} m \omega^2 q^2 \right] \phi(q) dq \ .$$

The field operator $\phi(q)$ can be expanded in a series

$$(24) \qquad \phi(q) = \sum_{n=0}^{\infty} b_n u_n(q) \ ,$$

where the b_n are (operator) expansion coefficients and the $u_n(q)$ are the complete orthonormal set of functions satisfying the equations

$$(25) \qquad \left(-\frac{\hbar^2}{2m}\frac{d^2}{dq^2} + \tfrac{1}{2} m\omega^2 q^2 \right) u_n(q) = (n + \tfrac{1}{2})\hbar\omega\, u_n(q) \ .$$

By substituting (24) and its adjoint into (23) and taking account of (25), we see that we can also write

$$(23a) \qquad H = \sum_{n=0}^{\infty} (n + \tfrac{1}{2})\hbar\omega b_n^{+} b_n \ .$$

We can also conclude immediately from (22) and the properties of the u_n that

$$(26) \qquad [b_n, b_m]_- = 0 \ , \qquad [b_n, b_m^{+}]_- = \delta_{nm} \ .$$

From Eqs. (23a) and (26) the meaning of the b_n^{+} and b_n may easily be deduced: they are the field-theoretical creation and annihilation operators for eigenstates of the Hamiltonian. If $|0\rangle$ is the physical vacuum state, then $b_n^{+}|0\rangle$ is a state in which one "particle" or <u>quasiparticle</u>, with energy $(n + \frac{1}{2})\hbar\omega$, is present; $b_m^{+} b_n^{+} |0\rangle$ is a state (not normalized if m = n) in which two quasiparticles, with energies $\hbar\omega(m + \frac{1}{2})$ and $\hbar\omega(n + \frac{1}{2})$, are present; and so on. The product $b_n^+ b_n$ is the number operator for the n-th eigenstate: it "counts" the number of quasiparticles having energy $\hbar\omega(n + \frac{1}{2})$. The number operator for the total number of quasiparticles in this vibrational mode is correspondingly given by

$$N = \sum_{n=0}^{\infty} b_n^+ b_n \quad . \tag{27}$$

It must immediately be observed, however, that even though we now have at our disposal the apparatus for constructing state vectors for states containing any desired number of quasiparticles, not all such state vectors are pertinent. The physical interpretation of the Hamiltonian (21) requires that each mode contain only one such quasiparticle in order that all the results of the second-quantized theory correspond to those obtained from the first-quantized theory described by the Hamiltonian (20a). It is interesting to note that if we had formulated our second-quantized theory in terms of the ions constituting the lattice then we would have had only a small number of field operators - one for each distinct type of ion (e.g., two for a diatomic lattice) - with a multiparticle state vector for each field. By converting our first-quantized Hamiltonian to phonon coordinates and then second-quantizing, considering each phonon coordinate to correspond to a distinct type of physical system, we obtain a large number of field operators but with only one particle present for each of these fields.

In studying the representative Hamiltonian (23a) it is therefore sufficient to restrict our consideration to the subspace of state vectors spanned by the vectors $b_n^+|0\rangle$, n = 0, 1, ... The connection between the second-quantized theory just introduced and the formalism of Section 3 is then easy to display. For this vibrational mode, the "raising and lowering operators" of Section 3, which are sometimes erroneously interpreted as creation and annihilation operators, take the simple forms [2], [8]

$$\begin{aligned} c^+ &= \sum_{n=0}^{\infty} (n+1)^{\frac{1}{2}} b_{n+1}^+ b_n \\ c &= \sum_{n=0}^{\infty} (n+1)^{\frac{1}{2}} b_n^+ b_{n+1} \quad . \end{aligned} \tag{28}$$

From these expressions it is easy to verify that within the subspace spanned by the $b_n^+|0\rangle$ the equality

$$\hbar\omega(c^{+}c + \tfrac{1}{2}) = \sum_{n=0} (n + \tfrac{1}{2})\hbar\omega \; b_n^{+} b_n$$

holds. The properties that c and c^{+} have, not of annihilating or creating a "particle" but merely of transferring it down or up respectively, to the next adjacent energy eigenstate, are quite clearly shown in these formulas.

In order to provide one final contrast between the field-theoretical creation and annihilation operators b_n^{+}, b_n and the one-particle raising and lowering operators c^{+}, c, we can note the difference between the matrix representations for c^{+}, c and those for, say, b_o^{+}, b_o. The matrix representations for c^{+}, c have already been given in Eqs. (10a,b). However, the expressions given there are just the submatrices for the case where the states on either side are one-particle states. For purposes of showing the mathematical nature of the quantities involved, it is convenient to consider the extension of the definition of c^{+}, c outside the physically significant subspace of the one-particle states for this vibrational mode. This can be done by using for these extended operators c_{ext}^{+}, c_{ext} the definitions given in (28), since these are meaningful even for multiparticle states.

To obtain an explicit matrix representation for the operators c_{ext}^{+} and b_o^{+}, we shall use as basis the vacuum state, the set of one-particle states, the set of two-particle states, ... , arranged in the order shown below:

$$(29) \qquad \left| \begin{array}{c} |0\rangle \\ b_o^{+}|0\rangle \\ b_1^{+}|0\rangle \\ \vdots \\ \frac{1}{\sqrt{2}}\, b_o^{+}b_o^{+}|0\rangle \\ b_o^{+}b_1^{+}|0\rangle \\ \frac{1}{\sqrt{2}}\, b_1^{+}b_1^{+}|0\rangle \\ \vdots \end{array} \right|$$

In order to clarify the form of the matrices obtained by using this basis, it is useful to divide these matrices into submatrices $[\ \ ]_{mn}$, where the labels mn mean that the matrix elements are taken between m-particle states on the left and n-particle states on the right. By using this notation and the basis (29), one may then write b_o^+ in the matrix form

$$
b_o^+ = \left[\begin{array}{cccc}
[0]_{00} & [0 \quad 0 \quad 0 \ \dots]_{01} & [0 \quad 0 \quad 0 \ \dots]_{02} & \dots \\
\begin{bmatrix} 1 \\ 0 \\ 0 \\ \cdot \\ \cdot \\ \cdot \end{bmatrix}_{10} & \begin{bmatrix} 0 & 0 & 0 & \dots \\ 0 & 0 & 0 & \dots \\ 0 & 0 & 0 & \dots \\ & \cdot & & \\ & \cdot & & \\ & \cdot & & \end{bmatrix}_{11} & \begin{bmatrix} 0 & 0 & 0 & \dots \\ 0 & 0 & 0 & \dots \\ 0 & 0 & 0 & \dots \\ \cdot & & & \\ \cdot & & & \\ \cdot & & & \end{bmatrix}_{12} & \dots \\
\begin{bmatrix} 0 \\ 0 \\ 0 \\ \cdot \\ \cdot \\ \cdot \end{bmatrix}_{20} & \begin{bmatrix} \sqrt{2} & 0 & 0 & \dots \\ 0 & 1 & 0 & \dots \\ 0 & 0 & 0 & \dots \\ & \cdot & & \\ & \cdot & & \\ & \cdot & & \end{bmatrix}_{21} & \begin{bmatrix} 0 & 0 & 0 & \dots \\ 0 & 0 & 0 & \dots \\ 0 & 0 & 0 & \dots \\ \cdot & & & \\ \cdot & & & \\ \cdot & & & \end{bmatrix}_{22} & \dots \\
\cdot & \cdot & \cdot & \\
\cdot & \cdot & \cdot & \\
\cdot & \cdot & \cdot &
\end{array} \right] \tag{30}
$$

On the other hand, c^+_{ext} has the matrix representation

$$(31)\qquad \begin{bmatrix} [\,0\,]_{00} & [\,0 \;\; 0 \;\; 0 \;\; \ldots\,]_{01} & [\,0 \;\; 0 \;\; 0 \;\; \ldots\,]_{02} & \cdots \\ \begin{bmatrix} 0 \\ 0 \\ 0 \\ \cdot \\ \cdot \\ \cdot \end{bmatrix}_{10} & \begin{bmatrix} 0 & 0 & 0 & \ldots \\ \sqrt{1} & 0 & & \ldots \\ 0 & \sqrt{2} & 0 & \ldots \\ \cdot & & & \\ \cdot & & & \\ \cdot & & & \end{bmatrix}_{11} & \begin{bmatrix} 0 & 0 & 0 & \ldots \\ 0 & 0 & 0 & \ldots \\ 0 & 0 & 0 & \ldots \\ \cdot & & & \\ \cdot & & & \\ \cdot & & & \end{bmatrix}_{12} & \cdots \\ \begin{bmatrix} 0 \\ 0 \\ 0 \\ \cdot \\ \cdot \\ \cdot \end{bmatrix}_{20} & \begin{bmatrix} 0 & 0 & 0 & \ldots \\ 0 & 0 & 0 & \ldots \\ 0 & 0 & 0 & \ldots \\ \cdot & & & \\ \cdot & & & \\ \cdot & & & \end{bmatrix}_{21} & \begin{bmatrix} 0 & 0 & 0 & \ldots \\ \sqrt{2} & 0 & 0 & \ldots \\ 0 & \sqrt{2} & 0 & \ldots \\ \cdot & & & \\ \cdot & & & \\ \cdot & & & \end{bmatrix}_{22} & \cdots \\ \cdot & \cdot & \cdot & \\ \cdot & \cdot & \cdot & \\ \cdot & \cdot & \cdot & \end{bmatrix}$$

It can be seen that the $[\;\;]_{11}$ submatrix of c^+_{ext} is identical with the matrix (10b) for c^+ which has already been given, as expected. Note that all $[\;\;]_{nn}$ submatrices vanish for b^+_o, as must always be the case for a creation operator; but the only nonvanishing submatrices for c^+_{ext} are of the type $[\;\;]_{nn}$. Similar statements obviously apply to the other b^+_n (and their adjoints, the b_n) as well.

Now that we have studied the properties of a particular one of the terms in Eq. (21), we can put the total Hamiltonian in the form

$$H = \sum_{k} \sum_{n=0}^{\infty} (n + \tfrac{1}{2})\hbar\omega_k \, b_n^{k+} b_n^{k} \tag{21a}$$

by simply adding the Hamiltonians of type (23a) for the various vibrational modes after first indexing them with the superscript k. By combining Eqs. (22) and (26) we obtain the alternative form

$$\left[b_n^k, b_m^{k'} \right]_- = 0$$

$$\left[b_n^k, b_m^{k'+} \right]_- = \delta_{kk'} \delta_{nm} \tag{22a}$$

for the commutation relations. It is then obvious that b_n^{k+} is a phonon mode creation operator for the k-th vibrational mode; when applied to the physical vacuum state it creates the k-th vibrational mode in its n-th energy eigenstate. Again let us emphasize that the action of this operator is quite distinct from that of the conventional c_k^+, which creates nothing but merely transforms an energy eigenstate of an already existing lattice to the next higher eigenstate. In this connection it should perhaps be mentioned that the "vacuum state" of the conventional formulation is not a state in which the lattice is not present (i. e., it is not the physical vacuum state) but is instead the state in which the lattice is present and is in its lowest energy eigenstate. For the k-th vibrational mode, for example, the conventional "vacuum state" is the state $b_o^{k+} | 0 \rangle$, not the state $| 0 \rangle$.

Finally, let us conclude our discussion of the harmonic lattice by observing that the energy eigenstates of this lattice, whose Hamiltonian is (21a), are obviously the direct-product states

$$\prod_k b_{n_k}^{k+} | 0 \rangle \quad .$$

5. Application to Interacting Systems

In the preceding section we have developed the second-quantized form of the theory of a harmonic lattice. In physical problems, however, the situations of greatest interest are those in which the lattice interactions are only approximately harmonic, but fail to be exactly so either because of the existence of an anharmonic component of the ion-ion interaction or because of interaction with another system such as an electron trapped in a lattice defect. The formalism introduced in Section 4 can easily be extended to cover these cases, and forms a powerful tool for performing calculations in such problems. In order to illustrate the techniques, we shall sketch the treatment of the theory for the case where the lattice interacts with one or more trapped electrons.

Suppose, then, that we have a system of N ions labelled s and M electr labelled i. We shall assume that the ions interact harmonically with one another, and that there is also an electron-ion interaction. However, the density of trapped electrons will be assumed to be low enough so that the electron-electron Coulomb interaction can be ignored. (Retaining the Coulomb term or anharmonic ion-ion interactions would entail no difficulties - at least, not as far as the formal development given here is concerned.) The first-quantized Hamiltonian for the system will then be of th form

$$\mathcal{H} = \sum_i \frac{\vec{p}_i^{\,2}}{2m} + \sum_s \frac{\vec{P}_s^{\,2}}{2M_s} + \sum_{s,s'} \sum_{\alpha,\beta} A_{\alpha\beta}^{ss'} Q_\alpha^s Q_\beta^{s'} + \sum_{s,i} W_s'(\vec{r}_i, \vec{Q}^s) \quad . \tag{32}$$

Here $\vec{r}_i$ and $\vec{p}_i$ are the position and momentum of the i-th electron, m is the electron mass, and the other symbols have the same significance as in Eq. (20). The first step we take is to again introduce linear combinations q_k of the coordinates Q_α^s so that the part of $\mathcal{H}$ containing only lattice variables is diagonalized. In the coordinate representation, Eq. (32) can then be rewritten as

$$\mathcal{H} = -\sum_i \frac{\hbar^2}{2m} \nabla_i^2 + \sum_i W(\vec{r}_i, q) + \sum_k \left(-\frac{\hbar^2}{2m_k} \frac{d^2}{dq_k^2} + \tfrac{1}{2} m_k \omega_k^2 q_k^2\right) \quad . \tag{33}$$

Finally, we expand the function W in a Taylor series in the coordinates q_k:

$$W(\vec{r}_i, q) = V(\vec{r}_i) + \sum_k V_k(\vec{r}_i) q_k$$

(34)

$$+ \sum_k V_{kk}(\vec{r}_i) q_k^2 + \sum_{k \neq k'} V_{kk'}(\vec{r}_i) q_k q_{k'} + \dots ,$$

where $V_k(\vec{r}) = \left. \frac{\partial W}{\partial q_k} \right|_{q = 0}, \dots .$

With this alteration incorporated, Eq. (33) takes the form

$$\mathcal{H} = \sum_i \left[-\frac{\hbar^2}{2m} \vec{\nabla}_i^2 + V(\vec{r}_i) \right]$$

$$+ \sum_k \left[-\frac{\hbar^2}{2m} \frac{d^2}{dq_k^2} + \tfrac{1}{2} m_k \omega_k^2 q_k^2 \right]$$

(33a)

$$+ \sum_i \sum_k \left[V_k(\vec{r}_i) q_k + V_{kk}(\vec{r}_i) q_k^2 + \dots \right]$$

$$+ \sum_i \sum_{k \neq k'} \left[V_{kk'}(\vec{r}_i) q_k q_{k'} + \dots \right]$$

$$+ \dots .$$

The transformation to an equivalent second-quantized theory can now be made just as in Section 4: we write down the expectation value of $\mathcal{H}$ for a product wave function, employing one wave function for each distinct component of the system; and we then replace each wave function by a field operator. We thus see that the second-quantized Hamiltonian corresponding to (33a) is

$$H = \int \psi^+(\vec{r}) [- \frac{\hbar^2}{2m} \nabla^2 + V(\vec{r})] \psi(\vec{r}) d^3x$$

$$+ \sum_k \int \phi_k^+(q_k) [- \frac{\hbar^2}{2m_k} \frac{d^2}{dq_k^2} + \tfrac{1}{2} m_k \omega_k^2 q_k^2] \phi_k(q_k) dq_k$$

(35)
$$+ \sum_k \int \psi^+(\vec{r}) \phi_k^+(q_k) [V_k(\vec{r}) q_k + V_{kk}(\vec{r}) q_k^2 + \ldots] \phi_k(q_k) \psi(\vec{r}) d^3x d$$

$$+ \sum_{k \neq k'} \int \psi^+(\vec{r}) \phi_k^+(q_k) \phi_{k'}^+(q_{k'}) [V_{kk'}(\vec{r}) q_k q_{k'} + \ldots]$$

$$\times \phi_{k'}(q_{k'}) \phi_k(q_k) \psi(\vec{r}) d^3x dq_k dq_{k'}$$

$$+ \ldots ,$$

where the $\phi_k(q_k)$ are defined as in Section 4, and $\psi(r)$ is the electron field operator and satisfies the anticommutation relations

(36)
$$\psi(\vec{r})\psi(\vec{r}') + \psi(\vec{r}')\psi(r) = 0 ,$$
$$\psi(\vec{r})\psi^+(\vec{r}') + \psi^+(\vec{r}')\psi(\vec{r}) = \delta(\vec{r} - \vec{r}') .$$

In order to write (35) in more manageable form, we can expand ψ and the ϕ_k in the series

(37)
$$\psi(\vec{r}) = \sum_j v_j(\vec{r}) a_j ,$$
$$\phi_k(q_k) = \sum_n u_n^k (q_k) b_n^k ,$$

where $\{v_j(r)\}$ and $\{u_n^k(q_k)\}$ are the complete orthonormal series determined by the equations

$$\left[-\frac{\hbar^2}{2m}\vec{\nabla}^2 + V(\vec{r})\right] v_j(\vec{r}) = \epsilon_j v_j(\vec{r}) ,$$

(38)

$$\left[-\frac{\hbar^2}{2m_k}\frac{d^2}{dq_k^2} + \tfrac{1}{2} m_k \omega_k^2 q_k^2\right] u_n^k (q_k) = \hbar\omega_k(n+\tfrac{1}{2})u_n^k(q_k) .$$

By replacing the field operators in (35) by their expansions (37), we then obtain the following expression for the second-quantized Hamiltonian:

(39)

$$H = \sum_j \epsilon_j a_j^+ a_j + \sum_k \sum_n \hbar\omega_k(n+\tfrac{1}{2}) b_n^{k+} b_n^k$$

$$+ \sum_{j,j'} \sum_k \sum_{n,n'} h_{jj'}^{knn'} a_j^+ a_{j'} b_n^{k+} b_{n'}^k$$

$$+ \sum_{j,j'} \sum_{\substack{k,k' \\ k\neq k'}} \sum_{m,m'} \sum_{n,n'} h_{jj'}^{kmm'k'nn'} a_j^+ a_{j'} b_m^{k+} b_{m'}^k b_n^{k'+} b_{n'}^{k'}$$

$$+ \ldots ,$$

where

(40)

$$h_{jj'}^{knn'} = \int v_j^*(\vec{r}) u_n^{k*}(q_k) \left[V_k(\vec{r}) q_k + V_{kk}(\vec{r}) q_k^2 + \ldots\right] \times u_{n'}^k(q_k) v_{j'}(r) d^3x dq_k ,$$

$\ldots$.

In this form it is easy to understand the physical meaning of the various terms in Eq. (39). The first two terms describe the system which would result if there were no interaction between the trapped electrons and the lattice vibrations; if only these terms were present, the eigenstates of H would be products of a lattice vibrational eigenstate and an electron eigenstate. However, the remainder of H destroys this "separability" of the lattice vibrations and the electrons. The third term introduces processes in which the electrons and lattice interact to produce a transition in the state of one of the lattice vibrational modes accompanied by a simultaneous change of state for an electron, the fourth term introduces processes in which there is a simultaneous change of state of one electron and two lattice vibrational modes, and so on.

In many cases of interest one can achieve sufficient accuracy (and a tractable problem) by retaining only those terms in the expansion of W in Eq. (34) which are of zeroth or first order in the q_k. In this approximation [3] H reduces to the form

$$H = \sum_j \epsilon_j a_j^+ a_j + \sum_k \sum_n \hbar\omega_k (n + \tfrac{1}{2}) b_n^{k+} b_n^k$$

(39a) $$+ \sum_{j,j'} \sum_k \sum_n d_{kjj'} a_j^+ a_j$$

$$\times \quad (n+1)^{\frac{1}{2}} (b_{n+1}^{k+} b_n^k + b_n^k b_{n+1}^{k+}) \quad ,$$

where

(40a) $$d_{kjj'} = \sqrt{\frac{\hbar}{2\omega_k m_k}} \int v_j^*(\vec{r}) V_k(\vec{r}) v_{j'}(\vec{r}) \; d^3x \, .$$

One can use this Hamiltonian as a starting point for the investigation of the properties of a system comprised of electrons trapped in lattice defects and interacting weakly with the lattice vibrations.

REFERENCES

1. See, e.g., Phonons and Phonon Interactions, T. A. Bak, editor, Aarhus Summer School lectures, 1963, W. A. Benjamin, New York (1964).

2. C. A. Coulter, D. W. Howgate and R. A. Shatas, Quasiparticle Conserving Hamiltonian for Interacting Electrons and Phonons, Phys. Rev. 140, A 2000 - 2002 (1965).

3. C. Alton Coulter, D. W. Howgate and R. A. Shatas, Fully Second Quantized Hamiltonian for Interacting Electrons and Phonons, Report RR-TR-64-18, U. S. Army Missile Command, November 1964, AD 455960.

4. D. W. Howgate and C. A. Coulter, Green's Function Calculation for Particle-Conserving Boson Systems, Transactions of the 11th Conference of Army Mathematicians, ARO-D Report 66-1, March 1966.

5. A. A. Maradudin, E. W. Montroll, G. H. Weiss, Theory of Lattice Dynamics in the Harmonic Approximation, Suppl. 3 of Solid State Physics, Academic Press (1963).

6. C. Kittel, Quantum Theory of Solids, Wiley (1963).

7. P. A. M. Dirac, The Principles of Quantum Mechanics, 4th ed., Oxford (1958).

8. M. Lax, Formal Theory of Quantum Fluctuations from a Driven State, Phys. Rev. 129, 2342 - 2348 (1963).

INDEX

INDEX